Water Bugs and Water Beetles
of Surrey

Water Bugs and Water Beetles
of Surrey

JONTY DENTON

SURREY WILDLIFE TRUST

Front cover photograph: *Acilius sulcatus* by Jonty Denton

ISBN 978-0-9556188-0-2

British Library Cataloguing-in-Publication Data.
A catalogue record for this book is available
from the British Library.

First published 2007
by Surrey Wildlife Trust
School Lane, Pirbright, Woking, Surrey GU24 0JN.

Produced by Flipside, Cranleigh.

CONTENTS

CONTENTS (continued)

CONTENTS (continued)

*"I feel like an old war-horse at the sound of the trumpet,
when I read about the capturing of rare beetles."*

CHARLES DARWIN

PREFACE

My own love affair with water beetles and bugs began in my childhood, when we moved to a farm in the Lake District which had a spring-fed, sandstone drinking trough. I wasted no time in digging out a large hole, which the spring rapidly filled. A day or two later the mud cleared and I was amazed to see a mix of all black and mottled yellow beetles feeding ravenously on the drowned earthworms. What were they, and where had they come from? I was hooked, and a few years later my PhD studies of the Natterjack and Common Toads led me to Woolmer Forest in Hampshire, which also supports our rarest diving beetle, *Graphoderus zonatus*. I named this species the Spangled Diving Beetle on account of its gorgeously golden spotted wing-cases. Studying this and the other species of aquatic bugs and beetles became a lifetime obsession.

Just what is the appeal of these beasts? Well it is very hard to put into words: the pure streamlined form of a diving beetle does more for me than any Ferrari, and the pursuit of our fauna will entail a tour of much of our great wild country from the Broads and coastal marshes to the tarns and lakes of the Highlands. Perhaps the greatest joy is that the season starts early and is a great cure for the winter blues. Delve around in mild weather in March and you will find things already in full swing, and long after the sun-loving 'bugs' of summer are gone, water beetles are still active right into winter.

Another crucial element to the psyche of the water beetler is the fact that ponds and lakes are finite entities, and knowing that your quarry must be in there somewhere is a powerful driving force, which I must confess is less strongly felt when searching for beetles in a grassland or wood.

The Great Diving Beetle, *Dytiscus marginalis*, is amongst the most familiar of insects, and has the distinction of having had the longest monograph on any invertebrate written about it. Korschelt's epic tome of 1948, 'Der Gelbrand' (Yellow-Edge), runs to a whopping 1827 pages of solid text and detailed figures of every part of the beast's anatomy!

The classic monographs on the British Water Beetles (Balfour-Browne, 1940, 1950, 1958) are also a somewhat turgid read! In this work I hope to showcase the beauty, character and behaviour of water beetles and bugs of all sizes, and give them the popular treatment they so richly deserve!

ACKNOWLEDGEMENTS

The maps were prepared with the DMAP program written by Alan Morton of Imperial College at Silwood Park.

Thanks to the following for contributing records, etc.: Max Barclay, Roger Booth, Sheila Brooke, Graham Collins, Andy Foster, Garth Foster, Andrew Halstead, Roger Hawkins, Peter Hodge, Mike Lawn, Dave Leeming, Ian Menzies, Bernard Nau, John Owen, and Andrew Salisbury.

Thanks to Franz Hebauer, Geoff Nobes and Paul Sterry for supplying photographs, and to Trevor Beebee for finding me yet more rarities to photograph, and for being instrumental in getting me started with water beetles!

Thanks also to Graham Collins and Matt Smith for help with producing the pond and stream density maps, to Roger Hawkins for his diligent proof-reading, and to Clare Windsor for her type-setting and other invaluable help with the production of this book.

I would also like to express my thanks for the ongoing support and financial commitment of Surrey County Council, and in particular John Edwards.

Finally, thanks to all the Surrey Atlas Committee members, especially Alistair Kirk, for their unstinting help and support.

LIST OF RECORDERS

AAA	A.A.Allen		DAL	Derek Lott
AEG	A.E.Gardner		DJC	D.J.Clark
AH	A.Hine		DJL	D.J.Leeming
AJC	A.J.Chitty		DL	D.Leston
AME	A.M.Easton		DS	D.Sharp
APF	A.P.Foster		EAB	E.A.Butler
AS	Andrew Salisbury		EAD	E.A.Duffy
BL	Brian Levey		EAW	E.A.Waterhouse
BSN	B.S.Nau		ECB	E.C.Bedwell
BSW	B.S.Williams		ECR	E.C.Rye
CET	C.E.Tottenham		EEB	E.E.Bignall

EJP	E.J.Pearce	KPB	K.P.Bland
ES	E.Saunders	LC	L.Christie
FB-B	Frank Balfour-Browne	ML	Mike Lawn
FDB	F.D.Buck	MP	Mark Parsons
FJC	F.J.Coulson	MS	Magnus Sinclair
FJS	F.J.Stephens	MVLB	Max Barclay
GCC	G.C.Champion	NT	National Trust
GEW	G.E.Woodroffe	OWR	O.W.Richards
GNF	Garth Foster	PH	P.Harwood
HH	H.Heasler	PJH	Peter Hodge
HSD	H.St.J.K.Donisthorpe	PSB	P.S.Broomfield
ISM	I.S.Menzies	RBA	R.B.Angus
ITE	Institute of Terrestrial Ecology	RDH	Roger Hawkins
		RGB	Roger Booth
JAC	J.A.Croft	RM	Rob Merritt
JAO	John Owen	RR	R.Richter
JAP	J.A.Power	SB	S.Brooke
JB-B	Jack Balfour-Browne	SLENHS	South London Entomological and Natural History Society
JC	J.Cooter		
JFS	J.F.Stephens		
JHB	J.H.Bratton	SRA	S.R.Ashby
JJW	J.J.Walker	TDH	T.D.Harrison
JL	J.Linnell	THB	T.Hudson-Beare
JLH	J.L.Henderson	WEC	W.E.China
JSD	J.S.Denton	WES	W.E.Sharp
KCS	K.C.Side	WW	W.West
KGB	K.G.Blair		
KNAA	K.N.A.Alexander		

SURREY – THE SURVEY AREA

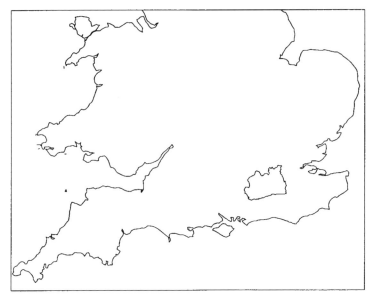

Surrey in relation to southern England

As with all the previous atlases in this series, the Surrey of this survey is the traditional county rather than the modern one. It dates from the proposal of H.C.Watson in 1852 to divide Britain into units of approximately equal size for the purpose of botanical recording. It is indeed fitting that Frank Balfour-Browne, the father of water-beetling in Britain, was a great champion of this method, introducing the 'Typo map' giving two-letter codes to each of the vice-counties.

Watson chose the county as his basic unit, but divided large counties into smaller units which he named vice-counties. Surrey was small enough to be kept as a single vice-county, whereas neighbouring Sussex, Hampshire and Kent are all divided into two halves, both of which are similar in size to Surrey.

The Surrey of this survey, known as the Watsonian vice-county 17, includes the following districts that are no longer part of the modern county of Surrey: the London Boroughs of Wandsworth, Lambeth and Southwark that were transferred to the London County Council in 1889; the London Boroughs of Richmond, Kingston, Merton, Sutton and Croydon that formed part of Greater London in 1965; Gatwick Airport, transferred to West Sussex in 1974.

The only significant part of modern Surrey outside our survey area is the

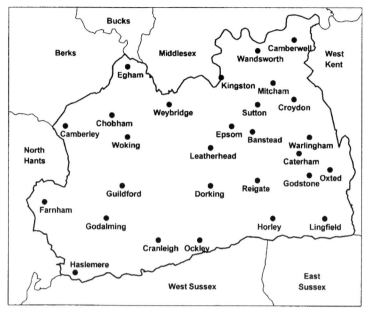

Surrey (Vice-county 17) in relation to bordering vice-counties

borough of Spelthorne, including Staines, Ashford and Sunbury, which is north of the Thames and was transferred from Middlesex (VC21) in 1965. The parish of Dockenfield to the south of Farnham is also part of modern Surrey although in the vice-county of North Hampshire (VC12). The construction of the A331 resulted in a slight diversion of the channel of the Blackwater which forms the county boundary near Lakeside Park, Ash.

In the north-east the boundary of the vice-county follows approximately that separating the London Boroughs of Croydon and Southwark from Bromley and Lewisham, but also includes the former urban district of Penge and the grounds of the Crystal Palace that are part of modern Bromley. The vice-county boundary differs slightly from the modern boundary between the boroughs of Southwark and Lewisham and can be followed by studying old maps. One problem area with the vice-county boundaries is the position of the islands in the River Thames (known as Aits or Ayts), some of which lie closer to the Surrey than the Middlesex bank, yet at present are nearly all considered part of VC21.

INTRODUCTION TO WATER BUGS AND WATER BEETLES

BUGS

The word 'bug' is often used as an overall term for all sorts of organisms from viruses and bacteria to many kinds of creepy-crawlies, but to the entomologist a bug is an insect of the order Hemiptera, and especially a member of the suborder Heteroptera or 'true bugs'. In Britain there are 68 aquatic bugs, and all are Heteroptera except the Pondweed Hopper, *Macrosteles cyane*, the sole aquatic hopper.

WHAT IS A WATER BUG?

Bugs, unlike beetles, have no pupation stage. The young bugs are neither larvae nor pupae, and are generally known as nymphs. After hatching from the egg, a bug goes through five nymphal stages, or instars. Each moult sees the body develop gradually towards the final adult form. The fifth-instar nymph often resembles the adult without wings. There are pros and cons for this form of development. The most obvious benefit is that water bugs do not need access to land to pupate, and can colonise water bodies around which beetles would be unable to develop. These include steep-sided water bodies such as horse troughs, but also sites with barren margins such as large open pools in sand pits and dune slacks. However, the disadvantages include the increased vulnerability to predators when in the soft transition phases between instars. One of the measures to counter this vulnerability is the development of a stink gland. Many terrestrial bugs are well known for their noxious emissions, but many Corixids have the same trick, which is all too evident when nymphs and adults are hauled out of the water in a net. Presumably the stink gland works well against aquatic predators, but I have never attempted to see how such emissions affect water quality, but you can certainly smell the outputs!

The nymphs of *Notonecta* are often glossy white or pale green (see Plate 5) and very conspicuous at least from below (their upper sides).

BEETLES

There are more species of beetles known to science than any other kind of life form. The order Coleoptera (which means sheath-wing) is named after the toughened wing-cases, or elytra, which are modified fore-wings. The hind-wings have remained the means of getting airborne, but life amongst the undergrowth required a means of protection for the delicate complex flight structures. The fore-wings thus evolved into body armour, and in the carnivorous water beetles they also became the casing for the diver's air supply. The ultimate in built-in aqualung equipment!

WHAT IS A WATER BEETLE?

In this book I have covered all the Coleoptera which spend at least part of their life-cycle in water (as adults or larvae) or on the emergent or floating leaves of water plants growing out of standing or flowing water. This includes all the purely aquatic families, the Gyrinidae (6), Haliplidae (16), Paelobiidae (= Hygrobiidae) (1), Noteridae (2), Dytiscidae (82), Hydraenidae (16), Helophoridae (18), Hydrochidae (2), most of the Hydrophilidae (40), and Elmidae (7), but also the semi-aquatic species of marsh beetle (Scirtidae (16)) which have aquatic larvae and terrestrial/arboreal adults, a ground beetle (Carabidae) with amphibious habits, the Georissidae (1), Heteroceridae (3), Dryopidae (6), and those leaf beetles (Chrysomelidae (22)) and weevils (Nanophyidae (1), Erirhinidae (8) and Curculionidae (35)) which have aquatic larvae or adults which live on water plants. This comes to a total of 283 species.

There is a somewhat grey area in such considerations. Some of the weevils and leaf beetles never get their tarsi wet. I have also included the three 'terrestrial' *Helophorus*, simply because there are so few records, and they are unlikely to receive coverage anywhere else! I have not included the terrestrial Hydrophilidae, Sphaeridiinae: *Cryptopleurum*, *Sphaeridium* and the dung-feeding *Cercyon* species.

It is worth mentioning other beetles which occur on, and/or occasionally enter water. The carabid *Oodes helopioides* hunts under water by crawling on submerged debris, etc. The tiny Camphor Beetle, *Stenus fornicatus*, also crawls below the surface film. Many of its cousins occur in wetland and are well adapted to a life above the water, for they can balance on the surface film and employ a unique means of propulsion to get off the water. They release a cocktail of surfactants from the tip of the abdomen, which lowers the surface tension resulting in the greater tension at the head end pulling them forward, often at great speed, until they collide with debris or vegetation onto which they can climb up and escape drowning. *Stenus* and other rove beetles will happily walk over floating plants such as duckweed, water-lilies and water fern. Other beetles which live exclusively on emergent aquatic plants include the small cryptophagid beetles of the genus *Telmatophilus*.

DIFFERENCES IN THE LIFE STRATEGIES OF BUGS AND BEETLES

The life cycles of some bugs enable them to exploit niches not occupied by breeding beetles. A visit to your local cattle-drinking trough provides a microcosm, which will illustrate one of the key differences in life history. Corixids and Notonectids are frequent inhabitants; indeed, *Notonecta maculata* is rarely taken in natural habitats but can abound in concrete, metal and plastic-lined troughs and open water tanks. Beetles, including *Agabus nebulosus* and *Hydroporus tessellatus* are often present in the same sites but are unable to reproduce successfully, simply because the steep bare walls of the containers prevent successful pupation.

Efforts to conserve our rarest native amphibian, the Natterjack Toad (*Bufo calamita*), have exploited this by using concrete-lined ponds with bare margins. The number of Dytiscids is drastically reduced and tadpole survivorship greatly enhanced, despite the attentions of the *Notonecta* adults and larvae.

BIOLOGY

PHENOLOGY, FEEDING AND REPRODUCTION

Adult beetles can be found at any time of year, but there is a marked slow-down in activity in cold weather, and some species hibernate for long periods in the mud at the bottom of ponds. The ease with which beetles can be captured by netting is clearly related to overnight temperature. When this is close to freezing, the beetles go down and it can be hard to find even the odd specimen of a species that was frequent only a day or two before in milder conditions. Sampling in mid December in Surrey can yield many species, as at Newdigate Brick Pits in 2001 when I monitored the colonisation of two new ponds constructed on 22nd November. Within a week the ponds contained water to a depth of 30cm, and by 23rd December they yielded 4 species. On 2nd January 2002 the water level had dropped considerably and the ponds were frozen solid! A front passed through in mid January and by the 25th they had filled to a depth of 70cm and yielded 8 species, including two which were Nationally Scarce. By 2nd February the species total had risen to 11! Winter is far from quiet for water-beetling! The first bugs to colonise were small Corixids which appeared in early March.

Some species can even be regarded as primarily winter-breeders; these include several *Helophorus* which use seasonal pools that dry up in early summer.

Agabus labiatus is often active in the winter months and most frequent in early spring. The larvae of *Dytiscus semisulcatus* are most active in late winter and are often fully mature in the spring. They feed on the larvae of caddis flies (Trichoptera), including species which breed in ephemeral ponds.

The effects of 'global warming' on water bugs and beetles in Britain are hard to ascertain, but in mid December 2006, adult *Gerris lacustris* and *Gyrinus substriatus* were active on ponds, almost a month later than my previous latest dates!

Adult riffle beetles can be found in rivers throughout the year, but numbers captured in the winter are greatly reduced.

Diet and feeding

A wide variety of prey items are taken by the carnivorous water beetles. Chironomids feature in the diets of many species. Molluscs are taken by both large and small Dytiscids.

Most Dytiscids and Gyrinid larvae have long pointed mandibles which they bore into their prey. These are furnished with tubes through which they inject a cocktail of paralysing poisons and digestive juices which break down the body matter of the unfortunate victim, which is then sucked back up through the tubes. Haliplid larvae feed in similar fashion but on algal cells.

Graphoderus and *Acilius* have larvae that prey heavily on cladocerans, and other small prey items, which they catch and devour by chewing in their jaws and swallowing in fragments. They may have only a narrow window when the prey is abundant. Indeed, studies of the Spangled Diving Beetle (*Graphoderus zonatus*), one of our rarest species, indicate that the population goes through large boom-and-bust cycles, being undetectable in some ponds in one year then present in thousands in the next. The 'booms' appear to coincide with years when water-fleas are superabundant during the peak of larval development.

The larvae of the non-carnivorous water beetles, including Helophorids and Hydrophilids, are carnivorous, although as adults they are mainly herbivores or detritivores.

Pupation

Unlike bugs, water beetles need to pupate on land. Some species appear to go through the winter in the larval state, and may migrate a considerable distance, presumably to avoid winter flooding. The larvae of *Ilybius fenestratus* were found over 20 metres from the edge of Mytchett Lake (Duffy, 1945). He dug up 14 larvae from under grass in mid March 1944. These were kept in damp soil in a beaker and were offered earthworms, which, surprisingly, some devoured. They began to pupate in late April, and the first adults emerged on 11th May. Remarkably, more larvae were found in the same place in the following February. These observations tie in well with the finding of numerous larvae of *I. fenestratus* in the winter diet of the Great Grey Shrike (*Lanius excubitor*) in Scandinavia.

Dytiscid pupae are active, regularly turning over within the cell, and react to light when exposed. Pupation varies in length from a few days to several weeks. Dytiscids typically pupate in soft substrates like sand, mud, and even decayed wood. The larva pushes material aside until a circular cell is formed, in which it pupates.

The larva of *Dytiscus semisulcatus*, featured in Plate 18, pupated on 16th May 2005, darkened on 5th June and emerged as a small but perfectly formed female on 9th June.

Longevity

Very little information exists on how long water beetles live, and most of what is available comes from captive adults. The record to date appears to be 5½ years for a female *Cybister laterimarginalis*, with female *Dytiscus marginalis* laying eggs after 2 and again after 3 years. Unnamed *Dytiscus* have reportedly survived for 5 years in Europe. At the other end of the size spectrum, the diminutive *Bidessus minutissimus* also survived for three years in a tumbler full of water with some fine gravel and a piece of waterweed; the only food added was a small supply of '*paramoecium and other minute living things*' (Balfour-Browne, 1962). I kept several *Bidessus unistriatus* in a small aquarium for over 18 months. John Bratton kept *Helophorus nanus* alive for over a year, despite it living in less than conducive circumstances on his work desk! *Helophorus* have terrestrial larvae, so it is possible that populations could ride out exceptional periods of drought in the larval stage. On the other hand, it may be impossible for them to delay development, so a different strategy is required, either through adults able to aestivate for long periods, or eggs that can tolerate desiccation. The latter strategy is found in some species of *Agabus*, including *A. chalconatus* which is often found in very seasonal pools formed in woodlands. The closely related *A. montanus* dwells in ephemeral heathland ponds, where its eggs can withstand prolonged drought (Jackson, 1958a; Carr & Nilsson, 1988). Both these *Agabus* species have adopted a strategy of passing the first winter in the egg stage and the second as adults.

The larvae of some beetles can aestivate for a few weeks if moist places such as the underside of stones are available in the otherwise dried-up pond basin. Adults can also be found aestivating, often in large numbers, beside ponds which had plenty of open water in the spring.

LOCOMOTION AND DISPERSAL

Swimming

All the true aquatic bugs swim from hatching through all the nymphal stages and as adults. Notonectids adopt an inverted stance and can be seen hanging face-up on the surface film. Corixids swim right way up. All use a sculling stroke with the legs employed together.

Many of the larvae of aquatic beetles are unable to swim and move around by crawling, but some are exceptional swimmers. Most of the larvae of the Dytiscids are accomplished swimmers. The large larvae of *Dytiscus* are easy to observe in open water where they progress by means of paddling all six legs. They are usually neutrally buoyant so can rise and fall in the water column. The larvae of *Acilius* and *Graphoderus* are the best adapted for life in open water, where they are sight-predators with the largest eyes of any Dytiscid. They move around with the balletic poise of a synchronised swimmer. The leg action is very rapid with 3 to 4 strokes a second, which can propel them at between 2 and 6 cm/sec., but they do not rely on speed to catch their prey but super-manoeuvrability. If threatened, they can employ a very different means of locomotion, which has led some people to call them skip-jacks. The muscles in the abdomen contract and the elongate body doubles up, so that the head ends up close to the underside of the tip of the abdomen. This rapid movement flicks the larva rapidly forward through the water by up to 5 to 6 cm. This can be repeated several times, carrying it clear of danger. This reflex is easy to observe if the larvae are netted, as they will attempt to skip even when out of the water.

Whirlygigs are extraordinary performers, and it is claimed that the swimming legs are the most efficient in the animal kingdom. The mid and hind legs of Gyrinids have developed into collapsible oars which are fringed with bristles. These work rather like a miniature Japanese fan, spreading out on the power stroke but feathering on the return stroke to provide very little resistance. It has been shown that the surface area of the hind leg changes from 1.625 mm^2 to 0.1 mm^2, a reduction of 94%. This is in itself remarkable, but when one considers that the fan-like hind legs open and shut up to 60 times every second, it is easier to understand just why this is such a marvel of nature. The middle legs are only used when the insect is disturbed or needs an extra spurt of power, but these still manage a blur-like 20 strokes a second! Calculations have shown that 84% of the energy applied to the water in the power stroke is converted into forward thrust, which is fairly meaningless until one realises that a turbine wheel (which drives most of our water-frequenting vessels) is only 55% efficient!

Gyrinids have a smooth swimming style in marked contrast to the jerky frog-kicking of Dytiscids. This is especially evident when the whirlygigs dive, when they often adopt a spiralling trajectory, especially when disturbed.

Clearly Gyrinids need senses which can match their superlative locomotive powers. When on the surface film the eyes are not especially useful in detecting prey falling onto the water; instead the ripples created by prey items and other whirlygigs are perceived by the antennae. The second segment is enlarged to accommodate a special sensory organ known as Johnson's Organ, which works as a direction finder and enables the beetles to pinpoint the source from which the ripples emanate. The antennae also act as a sort of built-in echo-location system akin to radar. The beetle produces a bow wave as it swims along and, if this hits another obstacle, it is reflected and part of the rebounding wave is sensed by the antennae. Despite it being able to swim over 40 times its own body length per second, the antennae enable the whirlygig to navigate with incredible precision, which explains why the members in the milling schools never collide. Cunning experiments have been devised to test the orientation skills of Gyrinids. Whirlygigs were forced to swim between linear obstructions spaced out a mere fraction wider than the breadth of the subject. The beetles passed through at speed without the slightest glancing contact with the sides!

Flight

The main factor controlling flight appears to be temperature and for many species the threshold temperatures are relatively high. For the whirlygig *Gyrinus marinus* a temperature of over 18° C is needed. This can be attained in cool weather by basking, and the absorption of solar radiation can help shorten the time needed to warm up the flight muscles which according to Johnson (1969) should reach 35° C.

In Sweden, 10km north of the Arctic Circle, *Dytiscus marginalis* was seen in flight at dusk when the air temperature was only 6.4° C. The water temperature was 8.4° C, and a male was seen making a humming noise which was closely followed by the wings flipping open and the insect flying off. This species has even been seen taking flight at temperatures of under 5° C (Nilsson & Svensson, 1992). Laboratory-based studies have shown that *D. marginalis* can sustain flight for 20 minutes, at speeds of up to 3m/second (Bauer & Gewecke, 1985). Flight at even lower temperatures is likely to be possible as *Colymbetes* have been observed in flight in Greenland in October! I have seen several *Helophorus brevipalpis* flying around ponds in December.

The Saucer Bug, *Ilyocoris cimicoides*, was until recently thought to be flightless in Britain, but over the past decade I and others have witnessed it in flight. It did not require exceptional temperatures to fly, so 'global warming' can hardly be invoked directly for the change. A more likely explanation is that flying forms have colonised from mainland Europe and mixed with the existing populations.

Little is known of the preferred timing of flight, but evening and night appear to be favoured by *Dytiscus marginalis*, although this species also flies by day as evidenced by the numbers taken by diurnal predators like raptors. Most of my encounters with larger Dytiscids have been on warm wet nights in spring and autumn. I remember sitting in my van (which had a black roof) one wet spring night when there was a 'ping' on the roof and an *Agabus bipustulatus* slid down the windscreen onto the wipers; within half an hour two more had done the same.

Netting ponds that are close to desiccation on a hot sunny day can produce spectacular results. In September 2001, I netted one such pond, and virtually every beetle, when exposed to the air, raised its elytra and flew off. What triggered this dispersal is not clear but, just a week or so before, I netted the same pond in similar warm weather but nothing took flight. All that had changed was the depth of the pond which had dried up considerably so that on the second visit it was impossible to net without scooping up the silty substrate.

Swarming behaviour is occasionally noticed, most commonly with *Helophorus*, but stream-breeders such as Elmids and Hydraenids can appear in some numbers, and seem to have a propensity to alight on red cars!

Many species disperse whilst still teneral, before the body skeleton has fully hardened. Species such as *Ilybius fuliginosus* are frequently taken in light traps in this teneral condition.

Most of the British Corixids are attracted to light, and on some nights the numbers of bugs raining down onto the sheet and entering the trap can run into the hundreds. It is remarkable how large numbers appear, even at traps remote from water, a few moments after the light is switched on. The numbers airborne on such nights must be astronomical! I cannot recall ever having swept a Corixid in flight, yet they do fly by day, but clearly favour nocturnal dispersal.

Flying is a costly and dangerous exercise in terms of energy resources and survival, so what are the pros and cons? Finding new breeding sites is often paramount for species inhabiting ephemeral waters. The autumn dispersal by large Dytiscids in Scandinavia has been associated with a move from small breeding sites to larger lakes where the adults are less vulnerable to death by freezing. This may have some credence as the phenomenon is not recorded in Britain and Ireland where the beetles are far less vulnerable in our mild winters.

Flying is likely to be a very risky strategy to the individual, but there is no doubt as to its effectiveness for populations. Despite this, the wastage must be huge. Large numbers of beetles are found on the strand-line around the Baltic, and I witnessed an extreme example of Nature's inefficiencies on the Atlantic coast of Argentina, south of Buenos Aires. Whilst strolling along the wide sandy beach I found a large Hydrophilid (very like our *Hydrophilus*) dead on the strand-line, and within a couple of strides a second; indeed, there was at least one freshly dead specimen along every metre or so of the beach front, which ran for several kilometres. The region was experiencing a long dry spell and the drought had presumably forced these beetles to look for pastures new. This had been going on for some time as the remains of this and other water beetles were present in the embryo dunes, and the next tide brought in a similar number of beetles which had presumably fallen, exhausted, into the sea and had died. *Hydrophilus piceus* has been found on oil rigs 65km off the East Anglian coast (Young, 1995), so crossing the channel is clearly within the range of our largest native species.

I constructed a small garden pond at Thursley in Surrey, which was filled with tap water through a hose. Before the pond was half full (after no more than 20 minutes) the colonisation from the air had already started. At least a dozen *Helochares punctatus* had flown in within an hour, and by next morning *Agabus nebulosus* and *Helophorus minutus* had also arrived. The nearest breeding site for *H. punctatus* was at least 800 metres from the new pond, so there must have been a considerable number of these beetles in the air on that unexceptional summer afternoon.

Haliplids, Dytiscids, Hydrophilids and Scirtids have all been taken at altitudes of over 200ft (Johnson, 1969) and some individuals have been taken from much higher.

The speed with which some species can colonise new territory is remarkable, and over the past two decades one species in particular has extended its range over a large area of Western Europe. *Hygrotus nigrolineatus* was first recorded in Britain in 1983, at Dungeness in Kent . Since then it has spread out across England and Wales, being first recorded in Surrey in 2001. It remains very local and is tied to new or recently cleared silt ponds, where it is usually taken with *H. confluens*. Other recent arrivals have become established in Kent (*Naucoris* and *Nebrioporus canaliculatus*), and may well spread in a similar fashion.

Several other species considered pioneers of new habitats have also undergone expansions, such as *Enochrus melanocephalus* which was formerly largely confined to coastal habitats but is now locally frequent in many inland sites.

Many of the species associated with marginal riparian habitats, such as exposed river sediments, are good fliers and behave more like pond species. Indeed, some *Heterocerus* are equally happy burrowing into pond and river banks. Other species may not be such effective colonisers, which has great implications for river management. The inhabitants of exposed river sediments have until recently been very neglected, but several recent studies have revealed how important this habitat is for many rare species. Unsympathetic river management can be very destructive to this fauna.

SURFACE-FILM DWELLERS

The inhabitants of the surface of the water are the most conspicuous of the species covered by this work. Pondskaters and whirlygigs are obvious to even the most casual observer, so much so that they have featured in poetry and prose of the likes of Hilaire Belloc and W.H.Hudson.

Guthrie (1989) provides a useful introduction to the insects that inhabit the surface film.

STRIDULATION

Anyone who has kept bugs and beetles in an indoor aquarium will quickly become aware of the extraordinary variety of clicks, ticks, zips and other noises which can be easily audible through the glass several metres away.

The Screech Beetle, *Hygrobia hermanni*, advertises its presence in the pond net by emitting a very distinctive 'squeak'. The sound is hardly a screech, but sounds like a short zip-fastener being rapidly opened and closed!

The method by which this sound is produced is described in no less a document than *The Descent of Man* by Charles Darwin (1899) whose description I cannot better:

"... *a strong ridge runs parallel and near to the sutural margin of the elytra, and is crossed by ribs, coarse in the middle part, but becoming gradually finer at both ends, especially at the upper end; when this insect is held under water or in the air, a stridulating noise is produced by the extreme horny margin of the abdomen being scraped against the rasps.*"

Berosus also makes clearly audible sounds. It is possible that these sounds may always (or in many cases) be primarily attractive.

Several other species have stridulatory files, but the sounds they produce are not normally audible, at least to my ears! These include *Agabus* and *Laccophilus* which have files on the underside of the abdomen, against which the hind legs can be rubbed.

Amongst the bugs the use of sound for communication is very well developed in the Corixidae. As its name suggests, the Water-singer makes enough noise to have entered the vernacular! This tiny little bug outshines the Wren when it comes to volume output against body size. The genus *Sigara* includes some of the best-studied 'singers'. The males of species such as *Sigara dorsalis* and *S. distincta* make two calls, mostly after dusk, and the calls increase in pitch with increasing temperature.

CHEMICAL DEFENCES

Anyone handling water beetles and bugs is likely to become rapidly aware of the means by which they attempt to avoid being eaten. The range of smells produced, even by the tiny Water-singers (*Micronecta*), are very pungent and can be quite nauseating.

The discharges of the larger Dytiscids are readily visible, as a bluish milky liquid which oozes out around the edge of the thorax. This is very pungent and lingers on the skin if it comes into contact with one's fingers. The discharges from tiny species like *Hydroporus neglectus* are sufficiently pungent to fill a whole room, as my family can testify. This is a defensive reaction and the secretion contains a cocktail of toxins, including the steroid hormone cortexon (11-desoxycordicosteron) which interrupts the sodium-potassium balance in vertebrates. If a predator such as a fish were to ingest this steroid, the effects would be severe and could result in narcosis and death.

Even medium-sized beetles like *Agabus bipustulatus* can produce copious amounts of toxins, and adult *Dytiscus* can store over 0.4mg of cortexon, which might not sound like much, but the adrenal glands from several herds of cows would be needed to extract a similar dose. Consequently, pharmaceutical manufacturers have looked at Dytiscids as an alternative source for the large-scale manufacture of such steroids.

Whirlygigs produce a similar milky substance into the water from glands in the abdomen. The purpose of this secretion is not fully known, but it is usually only produced when the beetle is threatened, and may act as a smokescreen in the manner of the ink of the squid.

The structure of the defence glands of the carnivorous water beetles was studied in great detail by Forsyth (1970). The pygidial glands of *Dytiscus marginalis* secrete a cocktail of chemicals; when out of the water, the beetles smear this all over the body surface. Some of these chemicals also act as water repellents.

In addition to these, the rectum of adult *Dytiscus* contains a foul-smelling liquid which is discharged when the beetle is handled out of the water; this is likely to be a defensive reflex (Crowson, 1981).

CAMOUFLAGE

Even a cursory glance through the plates is enough to see that there is a great variety of pattern and colour. The British Corixids employ some form of striped colouring, with most bearing patterns akin to tiger stripes on the upperside. The paleness of the pale stripes tends to increase in waters with light substrates such as sandy or silty pools. This is a form of adaptive camouflage.

I have long been puzzled as to how pale species avoid alighting in dark pools. The handsome diving beetle *Agabus nebulosus* is a strong-flying pioneer species, which not infrequently turns up in drinking troughs miles from any proper ponds. However, it rarely occurs in dark troughs, so presumably it is able to differentiate the substrate colour of troughs on the wing, and also have enough endurance to fly around long enough to find one (or a more suitable pond) to its liking!

Amongst the diving beetles the prevalence of strongly patterned species in open waters with little cover is well-known. In sparsely vegetated streams from highland burns to outback billabongs, a similar pattern emerges worldwide, with spotty or chequered markings prevalent on the upperside. This is thought to be a form of disruptive camouflage, where the beetle disguises itself by breaking up its outline. Sparsely vegetated stony-bottomed streams in England may support *Oreodytes sanmarki*, *Nebrioporus elegans* and *Stictotarsus duodecimpustulatus*, which, despite becoming increasingly large (at 2, 3 & 6 mm long, respectively), look superficially very similar. All three species vary in colour, depending on the substrate and degree of shading in their immediate surroundings. Plate 20 shows typical pale forms from open areas, and dark forms from partially shaded streams with dark substrates. *Platambus maculatus* follows a similar trend, from boldly marked (as in Plate 11) to very dark with only a hint of striping in dark shaded streams.

A similar trend can be found in open silt pools, where pioneer species such as *Hydroglyphus pusillus*, *Hygrotus confluens* and *H. nigrolineatus*, all of which look like fugitives from a humbug jar, often exploit barren-looking pools with little or no cover.

The undoubted champion of concealment is the Mud-coater Beetle, *Georissus crenulatus*, which actually coats its upper surface with sand and dirt (see Plate 22).

PREDATORS AND PARASITES

Birds

Avian predators of beetles are manifold: the larvae of Dytiscids have featured in the diet of Grey Heron (*Ardea cinerea*) in Hampshire, where I found a large partly digested bolus recently regurgitated by a heron. This contained a large number of well-digested fish fry, several Palmate Newts (*Triturus helveticus*) and three full-grown larvae of *Dytiscus semisulcatus* which the bird had consumed more recently, possibly from the adjacent heathland pond. A much rarer visitor to Thursley Moat Pond also partook of the local Dytiscid larvae. A Black-necked Grebe (*Podiceps nigricollis*) made a brief visit to Thursley Moat Pond on a memorable April day in 1991, and spent most of its visit diving for prey which included adult newts, dragonfly nymphs and, unmistakably, large *Dytiscus* larvae.

Adult Dytiscids come in a range of sizes to suit most insectivorous birds. One of the most impressive of all winged predators, the Hobby (*Falco subbuteo*), is legendary for its ability to take fast-moving prey from Swifts and Hirundines to Damselflies and Dragonflies. Large Dytiscids also feature regularly in the diet. These are eaten in flight and the wings and elytra are discarded, and on some large ponds they are carried by the prevailing breeze and accumulate on the shore. On Thursley Common I once found the remnants of over twenty *Dytiscus marginalis* and seven *D. semisulcatus* along a 25-metre length of shore in one afternoon. The occasional *Colymbetes fuscus* had also become a tasty in-flight meal.

In Europe the winter diet of the Great Grey Shrike (*Lanius excubitor*) occasionally contains adult Dytiscids, and, more intriguingly, the larvae of *Ilybius* have been found in numbers in some birds.

Wildfowl can have a marked effect on beetle and bug communities, not only through predation but also by habitat modification. Ponds with high densities of ducks and geese often (perhaps invariably!) support very impoverished faunas. The impact of artificially raising numbers of wildfowl was graphically illustrated on the Moat Pond on Thursley NNR in Surrey. This is a large and ancient water body which has been studied for many years. It supported a rich flora and fauna, including a relict population of the corixid bug *Glaenocorisa propinqua* and the scarce diving beetle *Dytiscus circumflexus*. In the mid 1990s the resident population of ducks and geese increased from a steady dozen or so to several hundred, attracted in by free hand-outs of stale bread brought, in some cases by the car-boot load, by misguided 'nature-lovers'! Within two years the marginal vegetation of the pond had changed beyond all recognition. The margins had once been fringed by extensive rafts of *Sphagnum* and floating St.John's-wort (*Hypericum elodes*), which were not only a delight to behold but abounded with water beetles and bugs. Even a brief dip of the net would yield a good variety of bugs and beetles. Today it is difficult to find even five species.

Plants

Perhaps the most bizarre instance of a water beetle meeting an untimely demise has to be that of a *Helochares punctatus* which had entered a pitcher-plant on Chobham Common. This North American insectivorous plant is well-established on a wet flush on the heath, and a wide variety of native insects had collected in the water-filled tubes, which, in addition to the unfortunate Hydrophilid, included the large longhorn *Strangalia quadrifasciata* and the Heather Beetle, *Lochmaea suturalis*.

Hymenoptera

This huge order of insects includes some which are parasites of various stages of Coleoptera. Chalcidoidea is a huge superfamily of mostly small parasitic wasps. Many aquatic species are known which parasitise the eggs of aquatic insects, especially Odonata, Hemiptera and Coleoptera (Jackson, 1956).

Two small families of winged Hymenopterans, collectively known as Fairy Flies, include species injurious to aquatic beetles. The family Mymaridae are diminutive winged Hymenopterans which are the smallest known insects, some measuring less than 0.5mm. These are capable of swimming under water using the oar-like wings for propulsion. *Caraphractus cinctus* is a relatively frequent species in Britain. The female has a long ovipositor which it uses to reach the eggs of various beetles including *Hydroporus*, *Dytiscus*, *Ilybius* and *Colymbetes*. *C. cinctus* can stay under water for over 12 hours without needing to surface, and quickly dies when exposed to air. The Eulophid *Mestocharis bimacularis* can also occur in large numbers in ponds and take a heavy toll of the eggs of *Dytiscus marginalis* (Jackson, 1964). Both these species have very short development times and go through several generations each year, and are most common in permanent weedy ponds where the hosts can lay their eggs in plant stems.

The Trichogrammatidae is a closely related family, with even smaller species including adults less than 1mm long! *Prestwichia aquatica* lays its eggs in those of beetles including *Hygrobia, Ilybius* and *Dytiscus*. The females have tiny vestigial wings and use only the legs for swimming.

Water Mites

The bright red larvae of aquatic mites are a frequent sight, sucking at the integumen of beetles and bugs.

Worms

Both Dytiscids and Hydrophilids are infested by nematodes, both internally in the body cavity and externally under the elytra. *Agabus* and *Hydroporus*, living in muddy water, are particularly susceptible (Jackson, 1973). Hydrophilids, including *Berosus*, *Cercyon* and *Anacaena* may have knots of worms under the domed part of the elytra. Beetles so infested are still capable of flight, so the worms can be regarded as phoretic, hitching lifts to new ponds, as was the case with *Hydrobius fuscipes* (Jackson, 1958b). The worms appear to invade the beetles' bodies in the water.

LAND USE, GEOLOGY AND DISTRIBUTION

Water beetles occur in virtually every aquatic habitat, from horse troughs to reservoirs, and from seepages to tidal rivers. The most obvious division of aquatic habitats is related to flow. Streams and rivers support species absent from standing water, and vice-versa.

Geology also has a marked effect on the distribution of many species. This is perhaps best illustrated on page 81 by *Agabus guttatus*, whose distribution coincides neatly with the boundaries of the underlying rock types.

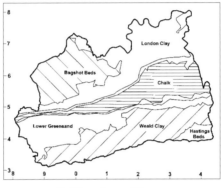

Solid geology of Surrey

Large areas of the chalk are devoid of any water bodies, and support no breeding water-beetle populations. Pioneer species are regularly crossing these areas in search of new homes, as can be seen in most cattle/horse troughs, but they are unable to breed in these steep-sided tanks. The only natural exception is the rot-hole-breeding *Prionocyphon serricornis* which breeds in the small pools of water that collect in the root tangles and rot-holes on trees, especially beech, which thrive on the thin chalky soils.

A few semi-subterranean species occur in springs, and man-made land drains.

Ground-water quality is profoundly affected by the bedrock through which it percolates. This is most noticeable where local enrichment leads to the development of 'poor fen' type habitats in areas of otherwise acidic mire as on Thursley Common NNR.

The heaths and commons in the west of the county support a distinctive assemblage of species, including many specialists confined to acid, *Sphagnum*-dominated pools over a peaty substrate.

Leached acid substrates support acid water bodies and streams. These waters are further acidified by the action of *Sphagnum* mosses, producing peat. In the past the cutting of peat for fuel created many open water bodies, both large and small. Small cuts rapidly re-colonise and support species typical of natural peat pools. Larger pools offer a wider range of niches for more open-water specialists, with the acidity preventing fish (which are very effective predators) from becoming established.

Natural pools and ponds are rare in Surrey, but fine examples include the Moat Pond at Thursley Common, which is thought to have formed as a periglacial feature and is home to a relict population of the corixid bug *Glaenocorisa propinqua*.

Shallow ephemeral pools on heathland, even small seasonal pools little bigger than puddles, have a distinctive fauna. Plants such as water purslane are characteristic of rut pools on trackways across heathy commons, and the fauna of these meagre waters is often surprisingly rich.

It is astonishing how pools teeming with beetles in early summer can be baked dry in the autumn. So much so that there is virtually no evidence of water ever having been present! The beetles cope by aestivating under logs or stones, or timing their pupation with the dry period, and emerging as the ponds refill in the autumn rains. Some species deposit eggs which are able to survive drought.

The lack of hard rocks in Surrey is not only manifest by the prevalence of brick as a building material, but in the rarity of stone and shingle in its water courses. One of the rare exceptions is the Paludina Limestone, or Sussex winklestone, which very locally forms shingle bars in streams in the Hazelbridge-Chiddingfold area.

The Weald clay has long been regarded as 'man's land', only workable by the hardiest of farmers, readily water-logging in the winter, and baking hard in the summer. As a result arable land is rare, and woodland and pasture prevalent. This resulted in the creation of field ponds to provide water for livestock. The map on Plate 1 shows that the highest density of ponds in the county occurs on the Weald Clay. It is no coincidence that this is also the stronghold of that doyen of old field ponds, the Great Crested Newt (*Triturus cristatus*), and several water beetles, including *Haliplus heydeni* and *Rhantus grapii*, show the same trends. The Weald Clay is also an important building material and the long and continuing history of its exploitation has left many opportunities for water bugs and beetles. The best current example is the former Newdigate Brick Works, where both large and small water bodies have been created in the old excavations. These now support one of the richest assemblages in the county, with scarce species including *Ochthebius pusillus* and the reed beetle *Donacia impressa,* for which this is the only known modern locality in Surrey. The large pondskater *Aquarius paludum* is a conspicuous inhabitant of the open lake surfaces.

The wooded streams on the Weald Clay are typically narrow, steep-sided and devoid of aquatic vegetation. Here, cover such as leaf litter at the margins or the submerged roots of the overhanging trees is preferred. Finding the occupants is a time-consuming and eye-straining process, but species like *Hydraena nigrita, H. rufipes* and *Ochthebius bicolon* are widespread in such situations.

The Wealden Iron industry left its mark on the Surrey waterscape in the form of Hammer Ponds. Valleys were dammed to create small lakes, which provided the power to drive hammers, crushers and bellows via a waterwheel at the outflow. Standing beside the tranquil Surrey Wildlife Trust reserve at Vann Lake, it is hard to imagine that this was once a hive of industry. But the reed beds around the margins support several scarce species, as does the splash zone around the old mill race.

Many industrial sites resulted in pond formation on the London Clay, but the expansion of the suburbs has resulted in the loss of many sites. In the preface to his 1908 *Highways and Byways in Surrey*, Eric Parker makes an apology for not covering the north of the county, explaining that:

> *"What was Surrey country a hundred years ago has been gathered into the network of London streets and belongs, in the mind and on the map, to London. Almost ten miles south of the London Thames the old Surrey countryside has disappeared."*

Ah! if only this were still the case, for the suburbs continue to sprawl. Those areas that have been protected support some of the richest assemblages in the county. Bookham Common and Richmond Park remain exceptionally rich, whilst the likes of Mitcham Common and Wimbledon Common are still diverse but have lost many of the rarer species. Other sites in the suburbs that have retained interesting faunas include Burgh Heath where the small ponds still support *Peltodytes caesus, Rhantus grapii* and *Enochrus coarctatus*, despite unwanted stocking by exotic plants and fish.

Aggregate extraction has also been highly beneficial for water beetles and bugs on other substrates. Flooded gravel pits are numerous along the Blackwater Valley and in the Thorpe area. Sand pits are dotted along the outcrop of the Lower Greensand right across to the Kent border. All these sites support a rich assemblage of pioneer species which exploit the open conditions in newly created or regularly disturbed pools.

The density of ponds across the county is shown on Plate 1. Pond densities are generally highest on the Weald Clay, which contrasts with the North Downs where large tracts of land are devoid of any standing surface water. Here beetles may turn up in water troughs, but with the exception of the Tree-hole Beetle, *Prionocyphon* (which thrives in small pools in the abundant mature beech trees on the downs), and is excluded from the coincidence map on page 37, few if any beetles can actually breed successfully. The creation of artificially lined ponds in otherwise dry areas means that there are more opportunities for stagnant water species and the 'downland desert area' is much smaller than that for stream species.

The distribution of streams is even more clearly influenced by the free-draining nature of the chalk-dominated North Downs, where huge tracts of land are devoid of any streams, even lavants or winterbournes (seasonal streams) (see Plate 1).

Large areas of the South London suburbs are similarly largely devoid of open streams, which in many cases have been covered and now flow underground and unseen.

Surrey's major rivers, the Mole and the Wey, have avoided the worst excesses of pollution, especially in their upper courses. The Wey in particular has remained in near-pristine condition and remains a national stronghold for rarities like the Golden Reed Beetle (*Donacia bicolora*) and the Artist (*Gyrinus urinator*), and supports local bugs including *Aquarius najas* and the River Saucer Bug (*Aphelocheirus aestivalis*).

Sand is carried downstream and deposited along the banks, often in large quantities. The SWT reserve at Thundry Meadows is a classic site for studying the effects of river dynamics on the beetle and bug fauna. Sand is deposited in the slack water on the inside of the loops and meanders. The moist sand exposed by the receding flood waters is home to a specialised fauna, including that ultimate master of disguise, the elusive Mud-coater Beetle (*Georissus crenulatus*), which blends into its habitat by carrying small lumps of it around on its back! The hairy burrowing water-beetles *Heterocerus fenestratus* and *H. marginatus* are attractive residents burrowing into the wet sand.

Areas enriched by the dropping of waterfowl attract rarities, including *Cercyon bifenestratus*. As well as the true water beetles, these sandy banks and accumulations of sand deposited around bridges, as at Brooklands, Eashing and Tilford, are home to many riparian specialists, including rove beetles such as *Stenus* and *Carpelimus*. These make a somewhat precarious living on the moist banks, and the non-aquatic species are vulnerable to drowning and have a powerful 'flee-response' which entails running as fast as possible up the slope to get clear of the rising waters. This reaction can be exploited, often with spectacular results. Splashing the bank with water can induce a veritable cavalry charge of beetles, some sprinting upwards, others, especially *Heterocerus*, emerging from the sand and taking to the wing. In many ways this is the best test of a beetle's true aquatic credentials, as the real water beetles make no effort to flee!

Chalk country has its own special flowing-water habitats. Land springs, or 'lavants', occur locally in Surrey, but the winterbournes, which are characteristic of the chalk country in neighbouring North Hampshire, are absent from Surrey.

All these streams flow only when the water table is sufficiently high to feed the channels. In dry periods the stream-bed can be bone dry, and this drought can last for several years. When the water does eventually break the surface, it can be short-lived and by midsummer dry conditions return.

Those species which frequent springs can often be found at the surface, as they are pushed out by the increased flows after heavy winter rain.

Canals

The heyday of construction came in the 18th and 19th Centuries and, until railway mania took hold, the canals were the motorway system of their day. There was a continuous network from Lancaster in the North-west through the heart of the Midlands and south to the capital.

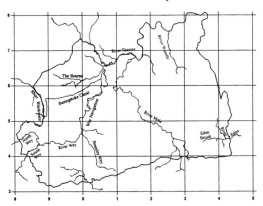

Surrey's major river and canal systems

There is good evidence that species have used canals to spread across the country. The influence of the canal network on the distribution of water beetles and bugs is hard to judge, as it was largely in place before collecting and recording insects became fashionable. However the distribution of *Ilybius fenestratus* in England and Wales fits well with the canal system. This species is almost always flightless, and is often abundant in the weedy margins of canals. Balfour-Browne (1950) discussed at length the history of records and concluded that ". . . *it looks as if the species has spread westwards and northwards* . . ." Of course canals and industry are inextricably linked, and new habitats such as gravel pits and subsidence ponds are also favoured by this beetle.

CONSERVATION

Thankfully the British water beetle fauna remains largely devoid of any exotic species; indeed, only the Azolla Weevil (*Stenopelmus rufinasus*) is an established New World species, first recorded in Britain in 1921.

The aquatic environment is especially vulnerable to increasing human population and all that this brings. The increase in building has led to the direct destruction, through draining, of many flood-plain wetlands. Other threats include loss of wetlands through lowering of the water table by groundwater abstraction. There is some evidence of this from wet heath areas, where ephemeral waters have had increasingly shortened periods of flooding.

The continued invasion of Scots pine on damp heath is also likely to have an adverse effect on the water table, and through the strong acidification of rainwater passing through the pine needles.

The stocking of ponds with coarse fish, and the introduction of domestic waterfowl and/or an increase in wildfowl density through supplementary feeding with bread handouts, can have catastrophic effects on wetlands.

The spread of alien waterweeds (often deliberately dumped by people clearing out aquaria and garden ponds) is so prevalent that most village ponds now have a very familiar look, with parrot's feather and swamp stonecrop dominant and choking out native plants. The latter is already a major headache on many nature reserves and is very difficult and costly to control, as even tiny fragments carried on dogs, boots and pond-nets, etc., are all that is needed to contaminate the next pond! Add to this the increasing problem of floating water pennywort, and the prospect for many of our rarer wetland plants and associated invertebrates is gloomy.

The effects of lack of management and simple neglect cannot be overstated, for succession leading to shading is a common and significant factor in the impoverishment of water bodies.

In all, 77% of the total historic beetle fauna of Surrey has been recorded since 1980; for the aquatics this figure is 86%, which would suggest that aquatic species have fared no worse than the Coleoptera as a whole. The bug fauna has seen a similar pattern.

SPECIES DECLINED OR INCREASING IN SURREY

Species which have become extinct in Surrey (excluding vagrants)

(? = species which may still occur as suitable habitats still exist)

BUGS

Hebrus pusillus ?

BEETLES	Last recorded	BEETLES	Last recorded
Haliplus variegatus	19th C	*Oulimnius troglodytes*	19th C
Gyrinus minutus	1908	*Donacia aquatica*	1912
Graptodytes flavipes	1965	*Donacia crassipes*	19th C
Nebrioporus assimilis	1866	*Donacia dentata*	19th C
Hydroporus rufifrons	c.1900	*Donacia sparganii*	c.1900
Stictonectes lepidus	1904	*Plateumaris braccata*	19th C
Laccornis oblongus	1901	*Bagous binodulus*	19th C
Agabus biguttatus ?	1912	*Bagous brevis* ?	1904
Ilybius subaeneus	<1830	*Bagous collignensis*	1941
Acilius canaliculatus	19th C	*Bagous limosus* ?	1946
Hydaticus transversalis	19th C	*Bagous longitarsis*	c.1900
Ochthebius aeneus	19th C	*Bagous glabrirostris*	1952
Limnebius aluta	1829	*Bagous lutosus*	19th C
Helophorus laticollis	1929	*Bagous nodulosus*	19th C
Hydrochara caraboides	19th C	*Bagous puncticollis*	19th C
Hydrophilus piceus	19th C	*Bagous tempestivus* ?	1929
Pomatinus substriatus ?	c.1900	*Bagous alismatis* ?	1915
Dryops similaris	1865	*Eubrychius velutus*	19th C
Scirtes orbicularis	19th C	*Lixus paraplecticus*	19th C
Oulimnius rivularis	1870	**Total = 39**	

Species which have seriously declined since 1950

Noterus crassicornis	*Graptodytes pictus*
Hygrotus versicolor	*Porhydrus lineatus*

Species which have significantly increased since 1950

Aquarius paludum	*Hydaticus seminiger*
Peltodytes caesus	*Ochthebius pusillus*
Hydroglyphus pusillus	*Berosus affinis*
Hygrotus confluens	*Enochrus melanocephalus*
Hygrotus impressopunctatus	*Helochares lividus*
Ilybius fenestratus	*Cercyon convexiusculus*
Rhantus suturalis	**Total = 13**

Species recently discovered to be resident and breeding

Haliplus apicalis	*Elodes tricuspis*
Oreodytes sanmarki	*Riolus subviolaceus*
Hygrotus nigrolineatus	*Donacia obscura*
Hydraena rufipes	*Pelonomus olssoni*
Helophorus alternans	*Rhinoncus albicinctus*
Helophorus longitarsis	
Cercyon bifenestratus	**Total = 12**

NEAR MISSES AND POTENTIAL SPECIES

Several other water beetles occur in neighbouring counties but have yet to be found in Surrey. Two in particular came close enough to actually get into the neighbouring part of a tetrad which is partly in Surrey!

Agabus congener (Thunberg, 1794) was taken at Sunningdale in 1889 (A.J.Chitty). Balfour-Browne (1950) gives this as Berkshire, but he is notoriously bad at placing sites in the London district in the correct county. This primarily northern species of peat pools still occurs in the New Forest and Emer Bog in South Hampshire, as well as at a site in Hertfordshire, so remains a potential species.

Berosus fulvus Kuwert, 1888 (formerly known as *spinosus* (Von Steven, 1808)) was taken at light just over the county boundary in Greenwich, but, as this is a rare brackish water species, any future occurrences in the county are likely to be of similar vagrants.

Species which have been taken in adjacent land-locked counties, but slightly further from the county boundary, include:

Dytiscidae

Hydroporus longicornis Sharp, 1871. This is known from Burnham Beeches and really ought to occur in Surrey. It is associated with spring-fed acid flushes.

Hydroporus marginatus (Duftschmid, 1805). A semi-subterranean species associated with winterbourne streams, especially on the chalk. Locally abundant in North Hampshire.

Agabus uliginosus (Linnaeus, 1761). Occurs in both North Hampshire and Berkshire in shallow seasonal fen-like habitats, which are rare in Surrey, although sites like Shalford Meadows look ideal.

Graphoderus zonatus (Hoppe, 1795). Deliberately introduced into two ponds in Surrey in the late 1990s, but a recent survey of these sites failed to detect any signs of the species. Unfortunately, both sites had deteriorated through lack of management.

Sphercheidae

Sphercheus emarginatus (Schaller, 1783). Formerly occurred in Middlesex and Berkshire but is now feared extinct in Britain.

Scirtidae

Elodes pseudominuta Klausnitzer, 1971. This may be synonymous with *E. minuta*, but is largely allopatric, occurring in more base-rich sites than *E. minuta*. It is recorded from most of the surrounding vice-counties, and really ought to be present in Surrey!

Psephenidae

Eubria palustris Germar, 1818. It is a pity that this, our only Psephenid, is absent from Surrey. It is a semi-aquatic species with larvae that develop in seepages and flushes. The adults are short-lived and can be swept from vegetation, including sallows.

Elmidae

Macronychus quadrituberculatus Müller, P.W.J., 1806. This is known from Surrey from sub-fossil material collected in the Thames, but it still occurs in the Thames and Kennet in Berkshire.

Chrysomelidae

Macroplea appendiculata (Panzer, 1794). This elusive and declining species occurs underwater on water-milfoil. It was recorded from Berkshire and Buckinghamshire in the 19th Century.

Macroplea mutica (Fabricius, 1792) occurs in brackish ditches, the nearest being from the Thames flood-plain in West Kent, where it can be found on fennel-leaved pondweed and eel-grass.

Curculionidae

Bagous tubulus Caldara & O'Brien, 1994. There are old records from Middlesex and it is still locally frequent in Kent. Associated with *Glyceria*, especially *G. fluitans*.

Bagous subcarinatus Gyllenhal, 1836. This was recorded from Middlesex in the late 19th Century. Associated with soft hornwort, *Ceratophyllum submersum*.

Neophytobius muricatus Brisout, 1867. The host plants of this rare fenland species remain unknown. It occurs a few miles to the west of the county in a valley fen beside the Whitewater at Greywell in North Hampshire.

Thryogenes fiorii Zumpt, 1928. This rare species is associated with *Carex* and is known from Burton Mill Pond in West Sussex.

Some other species are worth mentioning as possible colonists:

Micronecta griseola Horváth, 1899. Only recently recognised as British, although likely to have been overlooked and/or confused with other species in the genus. It occurs in the Kennet & Avon Canal in Berkshire and is highly likely to turn up in Surrey.

Cymatia rogenhoferi (Fieber, 1864). Recently discovered in Britain in Bedfordshire, and also found in Sussex. Larger and more parallel-sided than *C. bonsdorffii.*

Sigara iactans Jansson, 1983. I can claim a small part in the discovery of this species in Britain as I highlighted the possibility that it might occur on the basis of its discovery in Holland. Once the grapevine was alerted, it proved to be widespread in the east and could well turn up in Surrey.

Sigara longipalis (J. Sahlberg, 1878). Recently discovered in England and likely to spread.

Nebrioporus canaliculatus (Lacordaire, 1835) has recently colonised Britain (Carr, 1999) and is likely to spread like *Hygrotus nigrolineatus.*

Scarodytes halensis (Fabricius, 1787) has an unusual distribution across the Midlands, but is gradually spreading southwards and may eventually appear in the county.

IDENTIFICATION GUIDES

WATER BUGS

Savage, A.A., 1989.
Adults of the British Aquatic Hemiptera-Heteroptera: a key with ecological notes. FBA Scientific Publication No.50. Freshwater Biological Association, Ambleside.

Savage, A.A., 1999.
Keys to the larvae of British Corixidae. FBA Scientific Publication No.57. Freshwater Biological Association, Ambleside.

Dipsocoridae, Saldidae

Southwood, T.R.E., & Leston, D., 1959.
Land and Water Bugs of the British Isles. Warne, London.

WATER BEETLES

The most indispensable guide to identification of the fully aquatic water beetles is:

Friday, L.E., 1988.
A key to the adults of British water beetles. Aidgap series, Field Studies Council. This covers the Haliplidae, Gyrinidae, Hygrobiidae, Noteridae, Dytiscidae, Helophoridae, Hydraenidae, Hydrophilidae & Elmidae.

Gyrinidae, Haliplidae, Paelobiidae (=Hygrobiidae) & Noteridae

Holmen, M., 1987.
The aquatic Adephaga (Coleoptera) of Fennoscandia and Denmark. I. *Gyrinidae, Haliplidae, Hygrobiidae & Noteridae.* Fauna Entomologica Scandinavica, Vol.20. E.J.Brill/Scandinavian Science Press, Leiden & Copenhagen.

Dytiscidae

Nilsson, A.N., & Holmen, M., 1995.
The aquatic Adephaga (Coleoptera) of Fennoscandia and Denmark. II. *Dytiscidae.* Fauna Entomologica Scandinavica, Vol.32. E.J.Brill/Scandinavian Science Press, Leiden & Copenhagen.

Heteroceridae

Clarke, R.O.S., 1973.
Coleoptera, Heteroceridae. Handbooks for the Identification
of British Insects. Volume 5, part 2c. Royal Entomological
Society, London.

Scirtidae

Kevan, D.K., 1962.
The British species of the genus *Cyphon* Paykull (Col.,
Helodidae), including three new to the British list.
Entomologist's Monthly Magazine **98**: 114-121.
This figures all the *Cyphon* species which occur in Surrey.

Klausnitzer, B., 1992.
Scirtidae *in*: Lohse, G.A. & Lucht, W.H., *Die Käfer
Mitteleuropas*, Vol.13.

Klausnitzer, B., 1996.
Käfer im und am Wasser. Die Neue Brehm-Bücherei No. 567.
Includes a key to genera of Scirtid larvae.

Dryopidae

Joy, N.H., 1932.
A Practical Handbook of British Beetles. Witherby, reprinted
Classey. This remains useful and has male genitalia
illustrated, for most species.

Olmi, M., 1976.
Coleoptera – Dryopidae, Elminthidae. Fauna d'Italia,
Vol.XII. Edizioni Calderini, Bologna.

Chrysomelidae

Menzies, I.S., & Cox, M.L., 1996.
Notes on the natural history, distribution and identification of
British reed beetles. *Br. J. Ent. Nat. Hist.* **9**: 137-162.
Excellent key to Donaciinae, with colour photographs of all
species.

For the other Chrysomelids, including *Galerucella*, Joy (1932) remains
useful.

Nanophyidae (formerly part of Apionidae (Brentidae))

Morris, M.G., 1990.
Orthocerous weevils [Coleoptera: Curculionoidea (Nemonychidae, Anthribidae, Urodontidae, Attelabidae and Apionidae)]. Handbooks for the Identification of British Insects. Volume 5, part 16. Royal Entomological Society, London.

Erirhinidae and Curculionidae (*Hypera*)

Morris, M.G., 2002.
True weevils (part 1) [Coleoptera: Curculionidae (subfamilies Raymondionyminae to Smicronychinae)]. Handbooks for the Identification of British Insects. Volume 5, part 17b. Royal Entomological Society, London.

USEFUL ADDRESSES

Water Beetle Recording Scheme
Prof. Garth Foster, 7 Eglinton Terrace, Ayr, Scotland, KA7 1JJ

Scirtidae
Dr. Jonty Denton, 17 Thorn Lane, Four Marks, Alton, Hants, GU34 5BX

Water Bug Recording Scheme
Sheila Brooke, 18 Park Hill, Toddington, Dunstable, Bedfordshire,
LU5 6AW
Email: brooke.aquanet@btopenworld.com

STUDY SOCIETIES

The Balfour-Browne Club
Prof. Garth Foster, 7 Eglinton Terrace, Ayr, Scotland, KA7 1JJ

British Entomological and Natural History Society
Dinton Pastures Country Park, Davis Street, Hurst, Reading, Berkshire,
RG10 0TH

Amateur Entomologists' Society
P.O. Box 8774, London, SW7 5ZG

COVERAGE

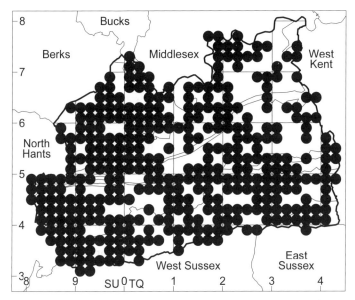

Distribution of tetrads from which records have been made
(excepting Prionocyphon serricornis)

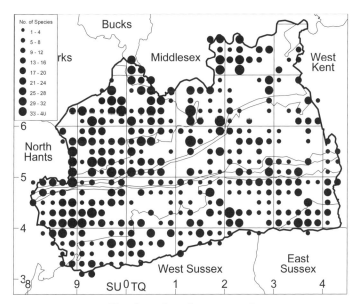

Number of species per tetrad

NOTES ON THE SPECIES ACCOUNTS

NATIONAL STATUS

Water beetles have had rarity statuses assigned to them across Great Britain. The statuses follow those published in Foster (2000) and, for weevils and leaf beetles, Hyman & Parsons (1992).

Endangered (RDB1)   Occurring only as a single population or otherwise in danger of extinction.

Vulnerable (RDB2)   Declining or in vulnerable habitat and likely to become endangered in the near future.

Rare (RDB3)   Very restricted by area or by habitat, or with thinly scattered populations, occurring in no more than 15 10-km squares.

Indeterminate (RDBIn)   Status information insufficiently known.

Nationally Scarce A   *(formerly Notable A)* Uncommon in Britain and occurring in between 16 and 30 10-km squares.

Nationally Scarce B   *(formerly Notable B)* Uncommon in Britain and occurring in between 31 and 100 10-km squares.

STATUS IN SURREY

Common   Occurs in most suitable habitats.

Widespread   Occurs widely in the county but is restricted to certain habitats.

Local   Found in no more than 20 localities.

Rare   Found at less than five localities.

DISTRIBUTION MAPS

Following the pattern established by earlier volumes in this series, the maps which accompany each account show species distribution as a pattern of dots within the boundary of the vice county of Surrey.

Each individual dot represents one or more records from an area two kilometres by two kilometres square, more commonly known as a tetrad. The dots indicate: ● – records 1970-2007 and ○ – records pre-1970.

The distribution of each species is plotted against either a simplified map of the county's main geological formations, or major rivers and canals, according to the habitat characteristics of that species. Maps are also overlaid with Ordnance Survey grid lines at ten kilometre intervals to enable readers to locate those sites described in the gazetteer.

HEMIPTERA – BUGS

DIPSOCORIDAE

Tiny predatory bugs which occur in wet places. A second species, *Cryptostemma alienum*, occurs amongst wet gravel in shingle bars in streams and rivers, primarily in the north and west of Britain, but it can also occur in the south.

Cryptostemma waltli Fieber, 1860 (= *Pachycoleus rufescens* Sahlberg)

Rare but under-recorded due to small size and cryptic habits. Adults occur in wet *Hypnum* moss, and are also found in *Sphagnum* moss.

RECORDS – **Godalming**, 4.5.1958 (DL); **Cosford Mill, Thursley**, in *Hypnum* near to marsh-marigold, 15.5.1960 (DL).

NEPIDAE – Water Scorpions

The Water Scorpion is an unmistakable insect: it is very thin for its size and the raptorial fore-legs are attached to the very front of the thorax under the small head and prominent eyes. It breathes through a long siphon-like tube which is a little over half the length of the body. This complex appendage (often mistaken for a sting) has, along with the fore-claws, given *Nepa* its popular name. The breathing tube is formed of two separate halves, which are held together but often come apart in dried specimens. Air is channelled along two grooves, which are covered in shallow hydrofuge hairs into which the spiracles open. The paler nymphs have a much shorter and blunt breathing tube. The upperside of the adults is a most vivid red colour, but could only be seen in flight (something British *Nepa* don't do!).

The Water Stick-insect is one of the most unusual and charismatic of our native insects, and the name is very apt for its looks and sluggish movements are reminiscent of a Phasmid. It can grow up to 35mm in length and the breathing tube, which as with *Nepa* is formed by pressing together two grooved appendages, is up to 20mm long. The fore legs are raptorial and *Ranatra* is a very patient 'sit and wait predator', which hangs vertically in the water column where its long body is camouflaged against the erect stems of emergent vegetation. The typical colour is a straw yellow, but nearly black specimens can be found, especially in peaty waters. It grasps passing prey in the fore-legs, which give it a prodigious reach, almost as long as the body. The fore coxae are greatly enlarged and could easily be mistaken for the femora. The tibia are quite short, and fold back to pin prey against the femora, which are armed with a short tooth which helps to secure the unfortunate victim. The mechanism is very similar to that employed by Mantids, and the middle legs are used to keep this high-precision killing equipment clean.

The range of prey taken is very diverse, ranging from water-fleas to sticklebacks! The former appear to be favoured but tadpoles and other insects (including each other) are also frequently taken. It is a good if somewhat inelegant swimmer.

The eggs of *Ranatra* are extraordinary (Plate 3) and are laid in rows in floating leaves and plant remains. The old leaves of reedmace and bur-reed are regularly used. The eggs are submerged or placed within tissues of waterlogged plant material, with the paired white hair-like breathing tubes sticking out above the water, looking like rough stitching!

Nepa cinerea

Linnaeus, 1758   PLATE 2

Water Scorpion

Widespread and common in ponds, lakes and canals, and at stream edges. Adults will emerge and walk over land, especially at night. It is invariably found at the margins of water bodies amongst litter and vegetation.

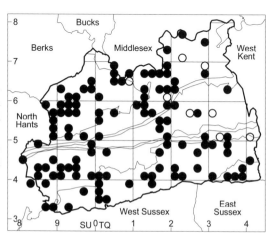

Ranatra linearis

(Linnaeus, 1758)   PLATE 3

Water Stick-insect

Widespread but local in ponds and lakes. Populations appear to be dependent on small fish or newts as prey. I had the good fortune to observe this species in flight in Surrey. It resembles a red damselfly with the body held parallel to the ground.

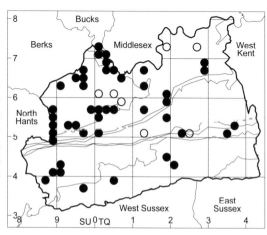

CORIXIDAE

Corixids are a group of totally aquatic bugs, which can be found worldwide. Two subfamilies occur in these islands, the Micronectinae (4 species), which are very small bugs, and the Corixinae (34 species), which are grouped into six genera: *Corixa, Sigara, Arctocorisa, Hesperocorixa, Callicorixa* and *Cymatia*. These are very similar-looking insects, so much so that they were all once placed in the genus *Corixa*. In all but one species, the markings on the upper side are a variation of yellow and black squiggles and spots, the exception being *Cymatia coleoptrata* which is plain brown.

Most species communicate by stridulating. This is often clearly audible, even up to 3m away. In captivity *Corixa panzeri* makes a variety of noises from single short 'tick' sounds to a regular 'zip-zip-zip-zip' noise made by rubbing the fore tarsi against the head. The different species have unique arrangements of pegs on the fore tarsi with which they can generate noise. Anyone keeping Corixids in an aquarium will quickly come to realise that theirs is a noisy world, but it is difficult to work out what is making which noise. The tiny *Micronecta* species must be among the most noisy creatures for their size in the animal kingdom, insects 2.5mm long which are clearly audible over 5m away!

Corixids are heavier than water so have to swim to the surface, and in warm weather these visits are extremely brief. They swim right-way-up and do little more than hit the surface film. From the water's edge, all the observer sees is a series of brown spots appearing and disappearing. The contact is much more rapid than any beetle or other water bug. Corixids surface less than similar-sized beetles, and carry a large supply of air under the elytra as well as on the underside of the head and body. With all this air on board, it is remarkable that they are heavier than water and can rest on the bottom without any need to anchor themselves to weed or similar support. Corixids overwinter as adults and can be seen swimming beneath ice-covered ponds.

Micronecta minutissima (Linnaeus, 1758)

National Status: Rare (RDB3)

Rare. A tiny bug found in open water at margins of lakes, large ponds and canals. Huge shoals of nymphs occur in the shallows, becoming adult in midsummer.

RECORDS – **Frensham Little Pond**, in open sandy shallows, 7.2000 (BSN & SB); recently taken in the Basingstoke Canal, but just inside Hampshire, 2001 (JSD).

Micronecta poweri

(Douglas & Scott, 1869)

Water-singer

Very local. A tiny Corixid which occurs in shoals at margins of rivers in quiet backwaters. It makes clearly audible sounds by stridulating, and is also very smelly when disturbed.

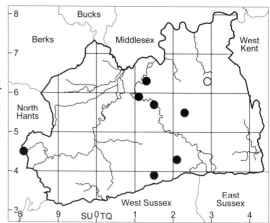

Micronecta scholtzi

(Fieber, 1860)   PLATE 4

Local, in open shallow waters over silt and sand.

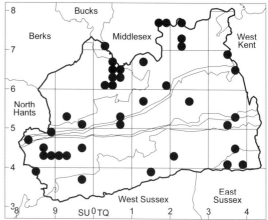

Cymatia bonsdorffii

(Sahlberg, C., 1819)   PLATE 4

Very local in still water, especially in acidic open water in large ponds, but also amongst submerged vegetation.

RECORDS – **Bookham Common**, 1931 (FJC); **Banstead, Pirbright & Epsom** in Groves (1983); **Moat Pond, Thursley**, 4.1998, 5.2005 (JSD); **Mytchett Lake**, 6.2001; **Black Pond, Esher**, 5.2001; **Thorpe Park**, 8.2003 (JSD).

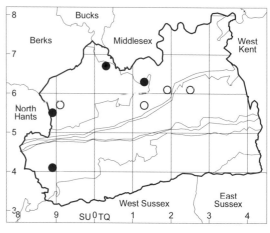

Cymatia coleoptrata

(Fabricius, 1776)   PLATE 4

Widespread but local in open water in large ponds and lakes.

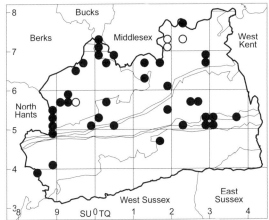

Glaenocorisa propinqua propinqua (Fieber, 1860)

Rare, a glacial relict species. The nearest current localities are in North Wales, Staffordshire and Norfolk, where it occurs in peaty pools. I have searched for it in the Moat Pond without success. The massive increase in wildfowl numbers and deterioration of the water quality may have had an impact on this vulnerable relic.

RECORDS – **Moat Pond, Thursley**, 1962 (KPB), 1983 and 1991 (JHB).

Arctocorisa germari (Fieber, 1848)

Local, perhaps increasing. In open water with no submerged macrophytes in sand and silt ponds.

RECORDS – **Richmond Park: Pen Ponds**, 21.3.1954 (DL); **Wimbledon Common: Kingsmere**, 23.8.1946 (EJP); **Thorpe**, 2002 (JSD); **Papercourt marshes** SWT reserve, 17.3.2005 (JSD).

Callicorixa praeusta

(Fieber, 1848)

Widespread and locally abundant in a variety of waters, including silt ponds and bog pools.

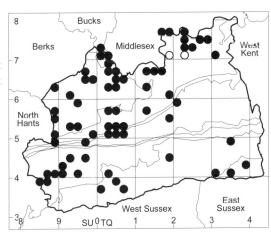

Corixa affinis Leach, 1817

Probably vagrant. Primarily associated with coastal habitats, including brackish pools, but it can occur inland, especially in newly created ponds.

RECORDS – **Oxshott Heath**, 7.5.1904 (AJC); **Bookham Common**, 4.4.1931 (FJC).

Corixa dentipes

(Thomson, 1869)

Local but somewhat under-recorded, in a wide range of still and slow-flowing waters. Often in company with *Corixa punctata*.

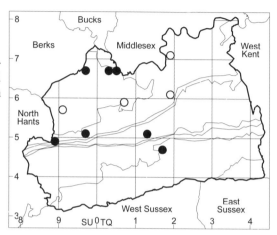

Corixa panzeri

(Fieber, 1848)

Chequered Corixa

Local in base-rich lakes, pools and ditches, especially in deep open water with rafts of weed. It also occurs in slow-flowing water. Seemingly absent from the Greensand and Weald Clay.

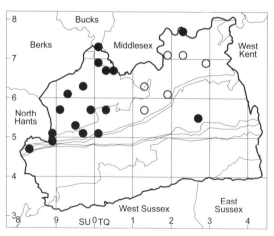

Corixa punctata

(Illiger, 1807)   PLATE 4

Common Corixa

The Common Corixa is the largest Corixid, being typically 12-14mm in length. It is a widespread and common inhabitant of ponds, lakes and canals, and occasionally slow-moving parts of rivers.

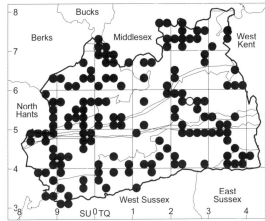

Hesperocorixa castanea

(Thomson, 1869)   PLATE 4

This small bug is locally abundant in peaty ponds and bog pools, often in very acidic conditions with pH less than 4.0.

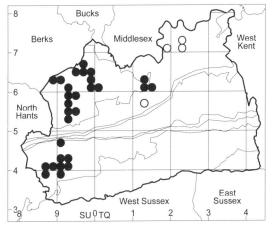

Hesperocorixa linnaei

(Fieber, 1848)

Local in base-rich ponds, lakes and canals with detritus. Frequent in ponds on the Weald Clay.

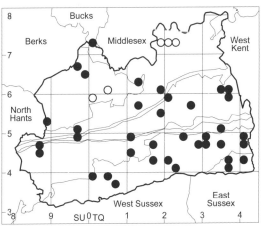

Hesperocorixa moesta

(Fieber, 1848)

Very local in base-rich ponds, especially in wooded areas. It can be locally abundant on the Weald Clay.

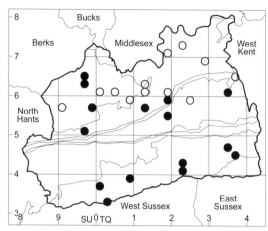

Hesperocorixa sahlbergi

(Fieber, 1848)

Widespread and frequent in detritus ponds, including acid peat pools and shaded sites. Also occurs in canals and at lake and river margins in calmer waters, and also in horse troughs.

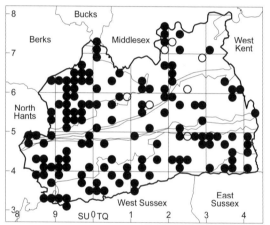

Sigara nigrolineata

(Fieber, 1848)

Common in silty ponds, including polluted waters such as farm ponds receiving enrichment from run-off from slurry and dung heaps.

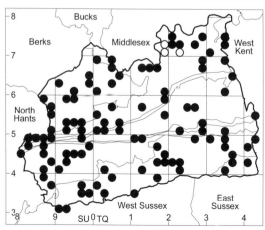

Sigara limitata

(Fieber, 1848)   PLATE 4

Local in relatively open water over silt in pools, canals, and drains, often in new ponds associated with aggregate extraction. Also taken at light.

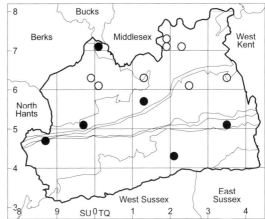

Sigara semistriata

(Fieber, 1848)

Rare in peat pools, including heavily shaded waters, with no post-1980 records, although it is still extant at an inland site in West Sussex.

RECORDS – **Horsell Common**, 16.9.1931(FJC); **Esher Common**, 1922-25 (OWR), 23.10.1951 (FJC); **Richmond Park**, 27.8.1946 (EJP).

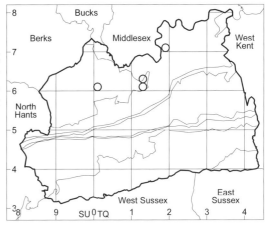

Sigara dorsalis

(Leach, 1817)

Frequent in a wide variety of ponds, ditches, lakes and canals.

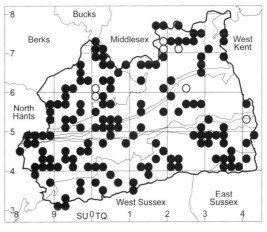

Sigara distincta

(Fieber, 1848)

Widespread and frequent in a wide range of waters, from detritus ponds and lakes to canals.

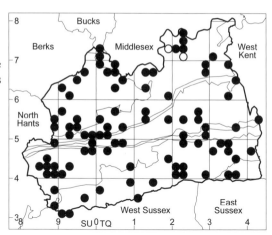

Sigara falleni

(Fieber, 1848)

Widespread and frequent in a wide range of waters, from detritus ponds and lakes to canals.

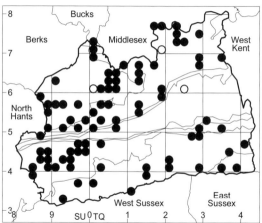

Sigara fossarum

(Leach, 1817)

Widespread but localised and seemingly absent from some areas. It occurs in a wide range of waters, from detritus ponds and lakes to canals, preferring base-poor waters but avoiding very acidic pools.

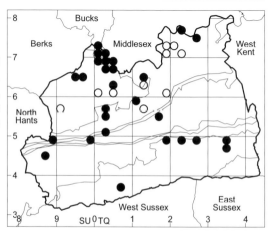

Sigara scotti

(Douglas & Scott, 1868)

Very local in peat ponds and bog pools, and occasionally in backwaters of streams. Often in open peat-stained water devoid of vegetation.

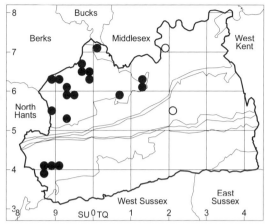

Sigara concinna

(Fieber, 1848)

Very local in open water in silt ponds, concrete-lined tanks, etc., preferring base-rich waters. Also at light traps.

RECORDS – **Esher Common** (GCC, ES); **Bookham Common**, 28.4.1951 (DL); **Banstead**, at light, 20.7.1952 (AEG), **Wimbledon Common, Kingsmere**, in bare pond, 23.3.1954 (DL); **Moat Pond, Thursley**, 22.6.1983 (JHB); **Surbiton Water Works**, in large concrete-lined settling ponds, 3-5.1998 (JSD); **Barnes**, 2000 (AH); **Fetcham**, 6.2000; **Newdigate Brick Pits**, 5.2000; **Thorpe Park**, 5.2003; **Longside Lake, Thorpe Green**, 6.2005 (JSD).

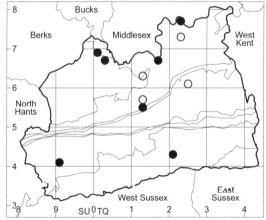

Sigara lateralis

(Leach, 1817)

Common in ponds and ditches, especially in organically enriched sites, including water which is fouled by livestock, and run-off from slurry, dung heaps, etc. Also common in horse troughs.

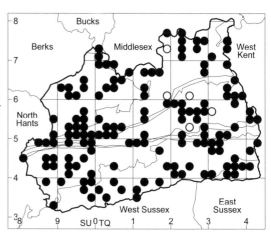

Sigara venusta (Douglas & Scott, 1869)

Rare, with old records suggesting an association with acid pools, which may well be the case with the Surrey records, although in recent years I have found it to be associated with base-rich running water (it is locally common in the Alre and Itchen, two chalk rivers of North Hampshire).

RECORDS – **Chobham Common**, c.1876 (ES); **Putney Heath**, 24.8.1946 (EJP); **Wimbledon Common**, 23.3.54 (DL).

NAUCORIDAE

The family Naucoridae is large and diverse and includes some of the biggest aquatic bugs in the world. In Britain we have only one common species, the Saucer Bug, *Ilyocoris cimicoides*. It is well named, being of a distinctive convex form, both as nymph and adult. It is a much more active predator than either of the British Nepidae. It is often one of the most abundant insects in the weedy margins of large water bodies such as marsh dykes, disused canals and lakes. And anyone wielding a net should be aware of it, since, like *Notonecta*, it can inflict a very painful wound with the rostrum. Toxic saliva contributes to the pain which in my experience is similar in severity to that of a wasp or a hive bee.

Adults overwinter in the water, and mating has been observed in early February. Eggs are laid in rows on water plants from March to May, and take up to two months to develop. By midsummer the last of the old adults have died off but the larvae, which are almost black in colour, can be extremely abundant, preying on water-fleas, gammarids and the water-louse.

They are powerful swimmers, using a similar stroke to *Corixa* and the *Dytiscidae*. On the bottom of the pond the fore-legs are used to root through the mud and debris. The bug can also run rapidly on dry land with the more typical hexapod motion of the middle and hind legs, which are less modified than those of many other water bugs.

The older literature usually describes *Ilyocoris* as flightless, but in recent years I have seen it in flight on several occasions.

A second species – *Naucoris maculatus* Fabricius, 1798 – has recently colonised England and may well spread as it is a strong flier.

Ilyocoris cimicoides

(Linnaeus, 1758)   PLATE 5

Saucer Bug

Widespread but local in ponds, canals and lakes. Adults overwinter in the water. The black nymphs hatch in April and develop through the early summer, with the new generation of adults maturing in June.

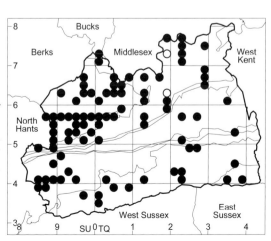

APHELOCHEIRIDAE

The River Saucer Bug is a distinctive flattened insect, adapted for life on the bottom of swift-flowing rivers and streams (and lakes in the north). It breathes via a plastron and so, unlike its relatives, never needs to surface for air. It is usually wingless (though a winged population has been found in the River Severn).

Aphelocheirus aestivalis

(Fabricius, 1794)   PLATE 5

River Saucer Bug

Apparently rare, but likely to be under-recorded as it occurs on submerged stones and logs in swift-flowing water, and also occasionally in marginal weed.

RECORDS – **River Thames: Runnymede**, 1990 (ITE); **River Wey: Broadmead-Pyrford**, 6.1999; **Newark Priory**, 4.2005 (JSD).

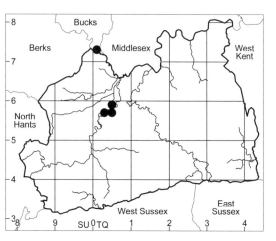

NOTONECTIDAE – Water-boatmen, Backswimmers

These familiar insects are good swimmers and fliers but have the special knack of hanging from the underside of the surface film and grabbing prey from beneath. Adults can take large prey, including the tadpoles of frogs and toads, and should be handled with care as they can inflict a painful wound with their powerful rostrum. *Notonecta* go through at least five instars. The last-instar nymphs have heads which are very similar to the adults, but the body is often a most distinctive pale green colour (see Plate 5). Four species occur in Britain, and all are widespread. *N. glauca* is a very common insect and there can be few water bodies of any permanence in which it has not occurred.

Notonecta glauca

Linnaeus, 1758   PLATE 5

Common Water-boatman

Ubiquitous in ponds, lakes and canals.

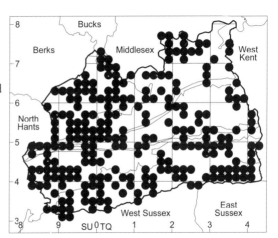

Notonecta maculata

Fabricius, 1794   PLATE 5

Peppered Water-boatman

Local in concrete water tanks, cattle troughs and bare stony ponds. The only 'natural' habitats in which I have repeatedly taken it in Surrey are in partially to heavily shaded weed-free streams, in deep plunge pools and quieter backwaters, especially on the Weald Clay.

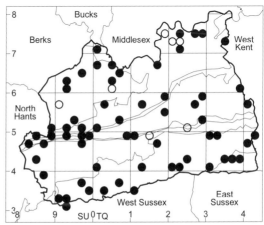

Notonecta obliqua

Gallén, 1787   PLATE 5

Pied Water-boatman

Local in peat ponds and acid bog pools, and occasionally but increasingly found in more base-rich sites such as clay ponds.

RECORDS – var. *delcourti*, **Ranmore Pond**, 4.2002 (JSD).

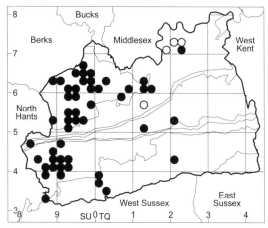

Notonecta viridis

Delcourt, 1909

Widespread in a wide variety of standing waters, especially in more base-rich sites.

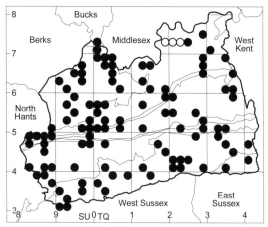

PLEIDAE

Plea is more likely to be mistaken for a beetle than any other water bug, being domed with a coarse punctured surface, rather like the sculpture on a golf ball. Adults are often of a creamy white colour, and swim upside-down like *Notonecta. Plea* is widespread throughout much of England and Wales but is only known from a single site in southern Scotland. Its favoured prey are cladocerans, and large aggregations of adults can be found in rich feeding areas such as rafts of water-milfoil, etc. *Plea* flies well, enabling it to colonise new ponds.

Plea minutissima

Leach, 1817

(= *Plea leachi* McGregor & Kirkaldy, 1899)

PLATE 6

Least Water-boatman

A tiny water-boatman found in weedy ponds, lakes and canals, often amongst submerged weed. It occurs in all kinds of ponds from acid *Sphagnum* pools to base-rich lake edges.

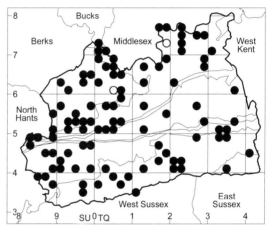

55

MESOVELIIDAE

The sole British species, *Mesovelia furcata*, is a small greenish insect a little over 3mm in length. It is found on mats of algae and floating leaves and on the water surface. It can be found on pondweeds (especially broad-leaved pondweed, *Potamogeton natans*), water-lilies and amphibious bistort, and may act as a pollinator of some of its hosts. The nymphs are superficially similar to those of water-crickets, but, being diurnal and denizens of open water, are unlikely to be confused. Most adults are apterous and usually found on well-established ponds. Both adults and nymphs are very active and can zip across the water surface or floating plants with great speed, and so are hard to catch. Nymphs are evident in May with the first new adults appearing in June, and some living on to November.

Mesovelia furcata

Mulsant & Rey, 1852   PLATE 6

Pondweed Bug

Local on large ponds and lakes, on leaves of water plants and on rafts of algae.

RECORDS (Post-1970) –
Barnes WWT reserve, 2000 (AH); **Bay Pond, Godstone**, 5.2000; **Moat Wood, Felbridge**, 2002; **Newdigate Brick Pits** SWT reserve, 2000 (JSD).

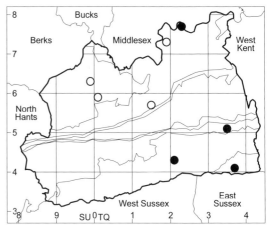

HEBRIDAE – Velvet Water Bugs

Two diminutive species occur in Britain. The Sphagnum Bug, *Hebrus ruficeps*, is a small velvety insect which is easily overlooked, but, if moss is pushed below the water surface, the bugs are readily floated out and appear at the surface. Despite its name it can be found in other mosses besides *Sphagnum* in more base-rich conditions.

Hebrus pusillus is often fully winged but is a much rarer insect than its congener. Despite this, the habitats at its few known localities are very varied. It has been found with *H. ruficeps* in *Sphagnum* around some New Forest pools. To my great surprise I found it walking around on slimy trickles on near-vertical clay cliffs in Dorset.

Hebrus pusillus

(Fallén, 1807)

Nationally Scarce B

Probably extinct. It occurs in a variety of wet places, including the margins of ponds, and seepages.

RECORDS – **Chobham** (GCC); **Wisley** (PH); **Merton** (JAP); **Barnes** (GCC).

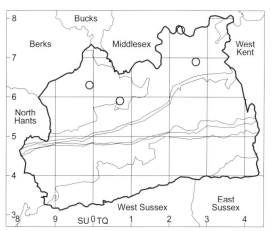

Hebrus ruficeps

(Thomson, 1871)   PLATE 6

Sphagnum Bug

A tiny velvety bug, half grey, half rust-red. It is very local amongst wet and partly submerged moss, especially *Sphagnum*, and also in litter in marshy areas as in Joyce's Meadow at Thundry Meadows. It is usually wingless, though winged specimens have occasionally been found.

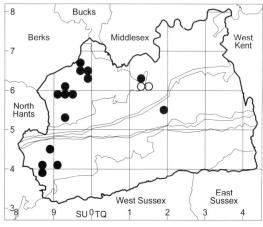

HYDROMETRIDAE – Water Measurers

Water Measurers are remarkable-looking insects, being the thinnest British insects in relation to their size. Bateman (1890) was reminded of Euclid's definition of a line, '*for they seem to have length, but no breadth to speak of*'. The stilt-like legs are even thinner and support the body above the water surface. *Hydrometra* walk on tip-toe, and their progress is usually slow, with the individual leg movements performed in a very measured way, '*as if pacing out the distance*' (Clegg, 1952). These delicate insects are also known as water-gnats, but this is an inappropriate name which is likely to cause confusion with certain groups of Diptera. The head is incredibly elongate and protrudes far in front of the eyes (see Plate 6). The main prey items are water-fleas and mosquito larvae which are pierced through the surface film and sometimes pulled up through it. The fore legs are not used to grasp or manipulate prey. The bugs can survive in ephemeral water bodies in very barren habitats such as chalk pits, where adults often shelter under debris for many months until the ponds refill.

A second species, *H. gracilenta*, occurs in Britain but has never been found in Surrey. It is a rarity of fens and other densely vegetated sites.

Hydrometra stagnorum

(Linnaeus, 1758)   PLATE 6

Water Measurer

Common at margins of ponds and streams, often found walking on the banks amongst vegetation as well as on the water surface. It can even be found on and under debris in dried-up water bodies in high summer. In 25 years of collecting I have seen only one winged example (in Kent in 2006).

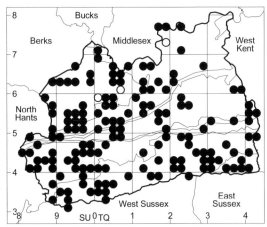

VELIIDAE – Water-crickets

Few bugs have adapted to life in swift streams, but the water-crickets, *Velia*, are an obvious exception, occurring in large aggregations on the calmer parts of streams. They skim around on the surface of still backwaters, where they feed on dead insects which have been swept or have fallen onto the water upstream. *V. caprai* is one of the most widespread and frequent species in Britain, being found on all but the most temporary streams. Most individuals are wingless, but occasionally winged forms appear.

Microvelia are all tiny denizens of densely vegetated places. The Minute Water-cricket, *M. reticulata*, is the only widespread species and can be abundant on the water surface amongst vegetation and litter. *M. pygmaea* is very local and southern, and *M. buenoi umbricola* is a great rarity of swampy places in East Anglia.

Microvelia pygmaea

(Dufour, 1833)   PLATE 7

Nationally Scarce B

Rare but likely to be under-recorded due to small size. Found amongst emergent vegetation and litter around still and flowing water.

RECORDS – **Woking**, 8.1875 (ES); **Chobham**, 7.1982 (DAL); **Bay Pond, Godstone**, 5.2000 (JSD); **Thundry Meadows**, in riverside sedge bed, 6.2000 (JSD); **Holmwood**, in weedy pond, 5.2001 (JSD); **Richmond Park**, 2001 (DJL); **Mill Lane, Godalming**, 25.5.2007 (JSD).

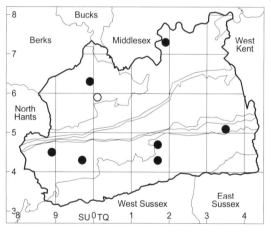

Microvelia reticulata

(Burmeister, 1835)   PLATE 7

Minute Water-cricket

Widespread and often abundant amongst emergent and floating vegetation at margins of standing and flowing water. Most individuals encountered are wingless, but fully winged individuals are not uncommon.

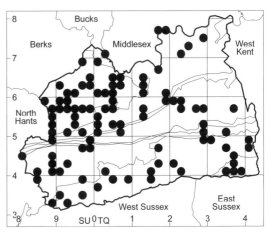

Velia caprai

Tamanini, 1947   PLATE 7

Water-cricket

Widespread on and at the edge of flowing water, and on lakes and occasionally on ponds and pools remote from streams. It is usually nocturnal in open situations but is regularly active by day on shady backwaters of streams, often in large schools.

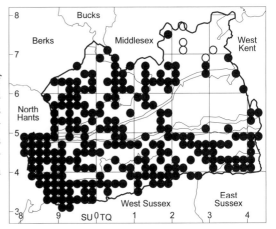

GERRIDAE – Pondskaters, Water-striders

Pondskaters, or water-striders, are highly specialised bugs. They have very long legs which help spread their weight on the surface film. The middle pair of legs are used like long oars and moved simultaneously to provide propulsion across the surface. The back legs are used as rudders for steering, whilst the short front legs are used to grasp and hold prey. Pondskaters are, along with the whirlygigs, the most familiar inhabitants of the water surface; in all, ten species are known in Britain. They can be found on virtually any kind of open water. Indeed, some species can even be found on the World's tropical oceans, and are the only true marine insects.

They feed largely on floundering invertebrates caught on the surface film. Adults overwinter on land and can be found in cracks in the brickwork of bridges or canal locks. Once Gerrids pair, they usually remain coupled throughout the breeding season, and the male must co-operate when the females climb below the surface to oviposit.

The upper surface is covered in a waxy coating which must be kept clean, and the bugs can often be seen flipping over to wash the upper surface. This is accomplished by employing a move akin to a self-tossing pancake; the whole process happens in a second and can be repeated several times in succession. The underside is covered in a fine layer of hydrofuge hairs.

Limnoporus rufoscutellatus (Latreille, 1807)

A very large species, which is a rare migrant.

RECORD – **Norbury**, 4.4.1893 (R.M.Leake).

Gerris argentatus

Schummel, 1832

Little Pondskater

Very local on ponds and ditches. On the Weald Clay it is locally abundant on large field ponds and small pools with open margins.

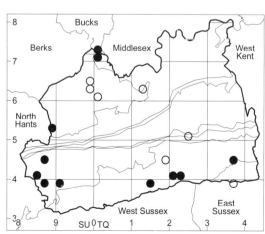

Gerris lateralis Schummel, 1832   PLATE 7

A rare species of densely vegetated wetland sites including swamps and *Carex* fen, often occurring amongst tall vegetation on very shallow water. Rare and scattered in southern England with two genuine records from Hampshire.

RECORDS – **Merton** (JAP); **Richmond Park**, Leg of Mutton Pond, 27.8.1946 (EJP); **Stafford Lake, Bisley**, 16.6.1974 (R.R.Fowell) – these records are given by Groves (1982), though not verified.

Gerris thoracicus

Schummel, 1832

This widespread species is usually readily distinguished in the field by the orange-red spot on the upper side of the thorax (though this is sometimes absent). It is somewhat sporadic on a wide variety of open waters.

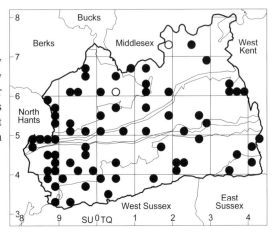

Gerris gibbifer

Schummel, 1832

Widespread, but commonest in acid water areas on heath pools, and also on horse troughs.

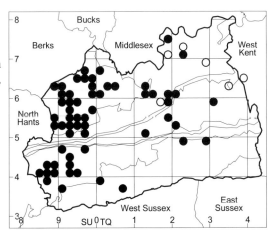

Gerris lacustris

(Linnaeus, 1758)   PLATE 7

Common Pondskater

Ubiquitous on standing water and the backwaters of streams. It can be found on the smallest water bodies such as horse troughs and puddles. It is invariably one of the first colonisers of new ponds, though I have never seen one in flight!

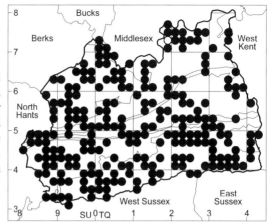

Gerris odontogaster

(Zetterstedt, 1828)

Toothed Pondskater

Widespread and frequent on a wide variety of standing waters. It often lands on small puddles. Wingless adults are frequent in summer.

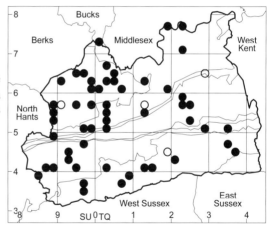

Aquarius najas

(Degeer, 1773)   PLATE 8

River Pondskater

Very local on flowing water,
especially on rivers where it often
occurs in large aggregations on
slack water close to more rapidly
flowing channels. The sheltered
water downstream from bridges is
a favoured habitat. It also occurs
at the edges of canals.

RECORDS – **Reigate & Woking**
(ES); **Chobham**, 1882 (EAB);
Ripley, 8.1900 (EAB);
Weybridge, 1925 (WEC);
**Basingstoke Canal: Pirbright
Bridge-Frimley Green**, 1954-5
(H.D.Swain); **River Wey:
Tilford-Thames**, 2000 (JSD).

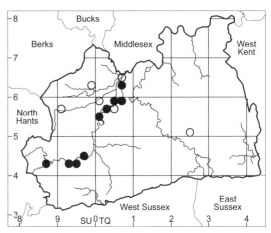

Aquarius paludum

(Fabricius, 1794)

Lake Pondskater

Nationally Scarce B

Widespread and spreading on large
bodies of open water such as lakes,
canals and large ponds. It is a
strong flier which can occasionally
turn up on small ponds and
puddles. Enormous populations
can build up on lakes, and in rough
weather countless thousands of
individuals are often forced to
aggregate in the quieter waters of
sheltered bays.

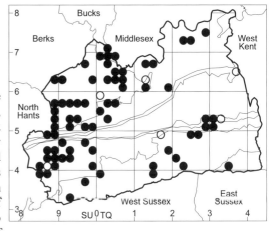

SALDIDAE – Shore Bugs

24 species occur in Britain, all but one of them at the margins of wetlands, with several in saltmarshes. The exception is *Saldula orthochila* (Fieber), a species of dry ground on downland, waste ground, etc. As the family name suggests, both nymphs and adults are superb jumpers, skipping to avoid capture, and, as the eminent hemipterist E.A.Butler remarked, *"Much hunting yields but few Saldas, and he who desires to cultivate the virtue of patience, cannot do better than try a day's Salda-hunting!"*

Saldula pallipes

(Fabricius, 1794)

Local on open sediments at margins of ponds and pools, especially on sandy clays on heaths, and also in gravel and sand pits, etc.

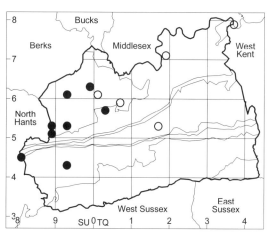

Saldula saltatoria

(Linnaeus, 1758)   PLATE 8

Common Shore Bug

Widespread and frequent at margins of standing and slow-flowing water.

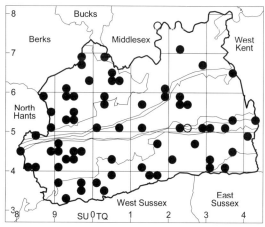

Micracanthia marginalis

(Fallén, 1807)

Nationally Scarce B

Rare in small damp hollows amongst heather, on *Zygogonium* algae. On Elstead Common it is part of a very rare community, also favoured by rare plants such as brown beak-sedge and marsh clubmoss.

RECORDS – **Woking**, <1900 (ES); **Chobham Common**, 7.1957, 11 & 21.6.1960 (GEW); **Esher Common**, 8.1957 (DL); **Elstead Common**, 12.6.1959 (AMM), 5.1997 (JSD); **Folly Bog**, 6.1997 (JSD).

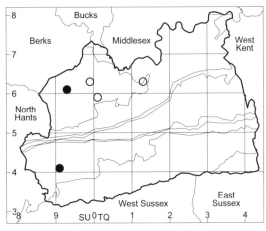

Chartoscirta cincta

(Herrich-Schäffer, 1841)

PLATE 8

Widespread amongst marginal vegetation and on litter around ponds, marshes and reedbeds.

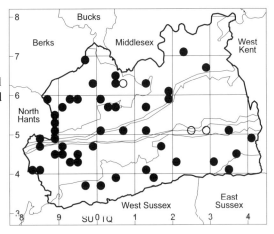

Chartoscirta cocksii

(Curtis, 1835)

Very locally abundant in *Sphagnum* in bogs and at acidic pond edges.

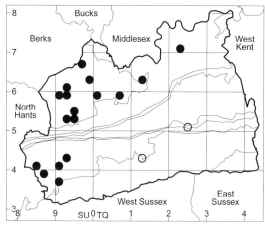

CICADELLIDAE – Leaf-hoppers

Macrosteles cyane (Boheman, 1845) PLATE 8

Pondweed Hopper

National Status: Indeterminate (RDBIn)

A distinctive blue leaf-hopper, which feeds on broad-leaved pondweed (*Potamogeton natans*). Adults and nymphs live on the floating leaves. Nymphs are present in mid to late May, becoming adult by mid June.

RECORDS –**Holmwood** (VCH); **Newdigate Brick Pits** SWT reserve, 2002, nymphs abundant on floating leaves, 27.5.2005 (JSD).

COLEOPTERA – BEETLES

Suborder ADEPHAGA

GYRINIDAE – Whirlygig Beetles

These are perhaps the most conspicuous water beetles, as they gather in schools on the surface of ponds, lakes and canals, gyrating madly when disturbed. Groups range from a few individuals up to huge assemblages of many thousands. When further disturbed, they can dive down through the water, being the ultimate in swimmers. It is claimed that the swimming legs are the most efficient in the animal kingdom. Living at the boundary of air and water poses its own special problems, and Gyrinids have one very special adaptation which allows them to make the best of both worlds. The eyes are completely divided into a dorsal and ventral portion, so they are effectively four-eyed!

Adults are carnivorous, feeding mainly on invertebrates trapped on the surface film. The distinctive elongate larvae prey on small invertebrates, especially bloodworms (Chironomid larvae) and Oligochaete worms. Once mature, the larvae move out of the water carrying a lump of debris with which they create a protective cocoon to shelter them through the vulnerable period of metamorphosis.

All *Gyrinus* have a very characteristic and strong 'yeasty' smell when netted or handled. Twelve species are currently on the British List.

Gyrinus aeratus Stephens, 1835

Nationally Scarce B

Rare, on open slow-flowing water. Basingstoke Canal, **Byfleet**, 1928 (K.G.Blair, confirmed JSD; two females and a male in HCC collections, Winchester). [Also occurs on larger lakes and slow-flowing rivers.] This species may well still occur in the county; it may be picked out in the field from *G. marinus* and *G. substriatus* by its slightly smaller size.

Gyrinus marinus

Gyllenhal, 1808

Very local, preferring larger water bodies, including large ponds, lakes and canal margins. It is frequent on the Basingstoke Canal.

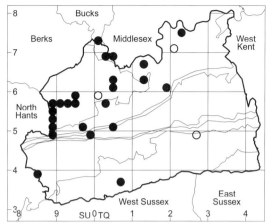

Gyrinus minutus Fabricius, 1798

Least Whirlygig

Nationally Scarce B

Probably extinct. Primarily a northern species of pools and small lakes on moorlands, etc. There are relict southern populations extant in Dorset.

RECORDS – **Esher Common**, <1902 (S.W.Kemp); **Oxshott**, 12.6.1908 (EAW).

Gyrinus substriatus

Stephens, 1828   PLATE 9

Common Whirlygig

Common on still and slow-moving waters, often forming large schools. Odd individuals can turn up on small ephemeral pools, though I have never seen one fly. Schools occur in both open and deeply shaded sites.

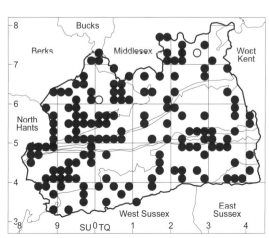

Gyrinus urinator

Illiger, 1807   PLATE 9

The Artist

Nationally Scarce B

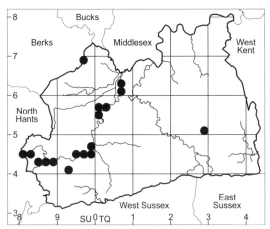

Easily identified by its red underside, the Artist is locally frequent in the River Wey and its tributaries. It is undoubtedly under-recorded, occurring, often singly, in and under rafts of weed or flood litter at margins of rivers and streams. It can occasionally be seen on the surface, having the odd habit of swimming to the surface as one's feet or net disturb the marginal weed, etc. At Thundry Meadows I found dozens of adults clinging to a partly submerged log. It can occur in deep shade under overhanging banks, especially in small streams at the head of the Wey. Strays are occasionally found on ponds.

RECORDS (outside Wey catchment) – **Virginia Water**, 1985 (RBA); **The Moors, Redhill**, 7.2001 (JSD); **Witley Common**, one on shallow pool, 20.3.2005 (ML).

Orectochilus villosus

(Müller, O.F., 1776)   PLATE 9

Hairy Whirlygig

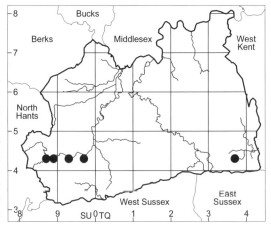

Local but probably under-recorded from flowing water habitats, especially those with overhanging banks. This flightless species is primarily nocturnal but can be seen by day on shaded streams making rapid sojourns out from the bank, leaving a characteristic sinuous wake. It is unusual in that it does not overwinter as an adult, and is therefore absent in the spring.

RECORDS – **Tilford**, 1984 (RBA); **Eden Brook**, 1990 (ITE); **Bagmoor Common**, 4.2001, **Stockbridge Pond**, 6.2001, **Mill Lane, Godalming**, 25.5.2007 (JSD).

HALIPLIDAE – Crawling Water Beetles

Haliplids are small but distinctive water beetles found in most aquatic habitats. They are good swimmers, employing rapid alternate strokes with the hind legs, and are also well adapted for crawling on submerged plants, etc. The diet varies considerably between species, with some adults carnivorous and others herbivorous, feeding on filamentous algae and charophytes (distinctive lower plants which are often confused with true vascular plants). All larvae feed primarily on filamentous algae. Nineteen species are currently known from the British Isles.

Brychius elevatus

(Panzer, 1793)   PLATE 9

Very local, but easily overlooked in permanently flowing water, especially in gravelly and muddy sections of streams and rivers with little weed.

RECORDS – **R.Mole** below **Box Hill**, 1926 (JLH), 2001 (JSD); **R.Mole**: **Cobham**, 1980 (JAO); **R.Wey, Tilford**, 1980 (RBA); **R.Eden**, 1999 (JSD); **Gibbs Brook**, 22.9.2000 (JSD); **The Moors, Redhill**, 7.2001 (JSD).

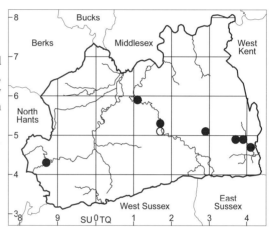

71

Peltodytes caesus

(Duftschmid, 1805)   PLATE 9

Nationally Scarce B

Local and scattered in richly vegetated silt ponds and flooded gravel pits. Usually in old well-established sites, but it also occurs in quite new water bodies in Berkshire and North Hampshire.

RECORDS – **Wandsworth Common**, 1820 (A.Ingpen); **Battersea Fields**, 1839 (JFS); **Mitcham Common**, 1927

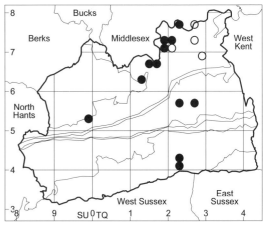

(JLH); **Surbiton, old water works**, 4.1998; **Weston Green**, 5.1999; **Elmore Pond**, 5.2000 (JSD); **Barnes WWT Centre**, 2000 (AH); **Richmond Park**, 5.2001 (DJL); **Cudworth**, 4.2001; **Edolphs Copse**, 5.2001; **Whitmoor Common**, 17.3.2005; **Burgh Heath**, 21.3.2005 (JSD).

Haliplus apicalis Thomson, C.G., 1868

Nationally Scarce B

A halophile, associated with pools and ditches which occasionally suffer tidal inundation. Found at **Barnes** in ditches on the Wildfowl and Wetlands Trust Reserve (Adrian Hine) in 2000.

Haliplus confinis

Stephens, 1828

Rather local in silt ponds and gravel pits, often with charophytes. Gravel pits in the Blackwater Valley and Thorpe district are strongholds.

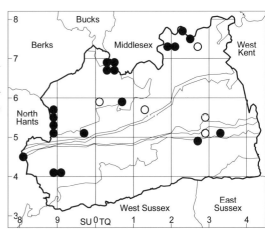

Haliplus flavicollis

Sturm, 1834   PLATE 9

Distinguished by its large size, heavily punctured body and pale colouring, it is a local species of the larger ponds and canals, especially if sparsely vegetated.

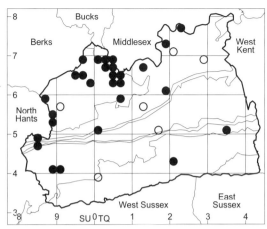

Haliplus fluviatilis

Aubé, 1836

Widespread in flowing water and gravel pit ponds.

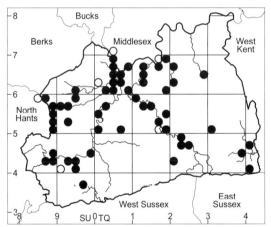

Haliplus fulvus

(Fabricius, 1801)

This, the largest *Haliplus* in Surrey, is a very local species, found in large ponds, small lakes and canals.

RECORDS – **Wandsworth Common**, 1820 (A.Ingpen); **Earlswood**, 1850s (JL); **Richmond Park**, 1900 (HSD); **Mitcham Common**, 1920-27 (JLH); **Wisley**, 1920 (JLH); **Bookham Common**, 1932 (FJC), 11.2.1997 (MVLB); **Bolder Mere**, 1976 (JAO), 2000 (JSD); **Headley Heath**, 1980 (JAO); **Langham Pond**, 1988 (RBA); **Basingstoke Canal** (SU8953), 1988 (RM); **Moat Pond, Thursley**, 1995-2000 (JSD).

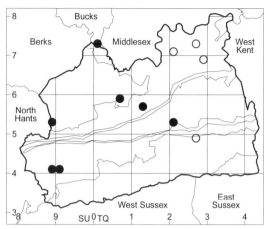

Haliplus heydeni

Wehncke, 1875

Nationally Scarce B

Very local in small well-vegetated ponds, it has persisted in a small butyl-lined garden pond at Thursley for many years. Tolerant of some shading.

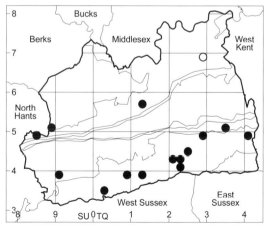

Haliplus immaculatus

Gerhardt, 1877

Widespread in base-rich lakes and ponds, and in the Basingstoke Canal. Absent from heathy districts.

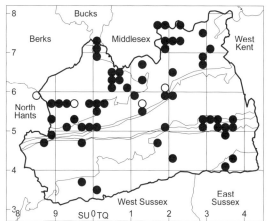

Haliplus laminatus

(Schaller, 1783)

Nationally Scarce B

Local at margins of flowing water, and in gravel pits and canals. It can thrive in built-up areas, providing water quality is reasonable, although it also occurs in moderately polluted waters.

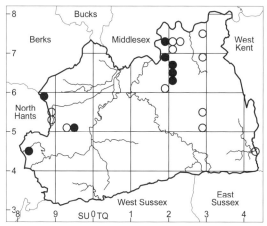

Haliplus lineatocollis

(Marsham, 1802)   PLATE 10

This distinctive species, with characteristic markings on the thorax, is widespread and often abundant in all kinds of flowing water habitats. It is common in chalk streams and at weedy canal margins, and is also found regularly in ponds, especially new ones.

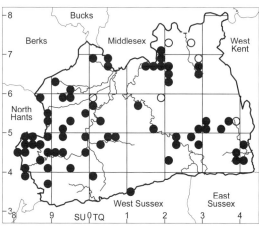

Haliplus lineolatus

Mannerheim, 1844

Rare in weedy base-rich ponds, and also in the well-vegetated sections of the Basingstoke Canal.

RECORDS – **Frensham**, 1929; **Blackwater Valley**, 1930 (EJP); **Brookwood**, 1938 (FJC); **Bay Pond** SWT reserve, 5.2000; **Thorpe Park**, 4.2003 (JSD).

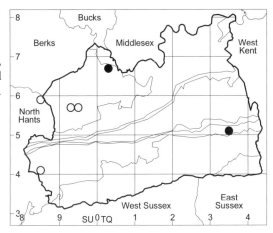

Haliplus obliquus

(Fabricius, 1787)   PLATE 10

Perhaps the most distinctive and handsome British Haliplid, the chequer-marked *H. obliquus* is a rare species in Surrey, associated with nutrient-rich waters with abundant charophytes (*Chara* species). It is a good coloniser of new sites such as old aggregate workings, but often fades out as these sites mature and higher plants take over.

RECORDS – **Earlswood**, 1851 (JL); **Wimbledon** (JAP); **Esher** (JAP); **Cutt Mill**, 1905 (JAC); **Bookham Common**, 1932 (FJC); **Oxshott**, 1948 (AAA); **Partridge Farm, near Staffhurst Wood**, 5.2000 (JSD); **The Moors, Redhill**, in sandpit, 7.2001 (JSD).

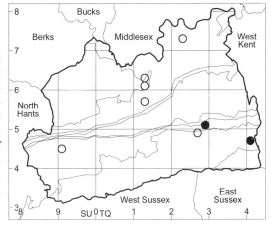

Haliplus ruficollis

(Degeer, 1774)   PLATE 10

Widespread and locally frequent in richly vegetated ponds, and canals. The only Haliplid commonly found in heathland pools.

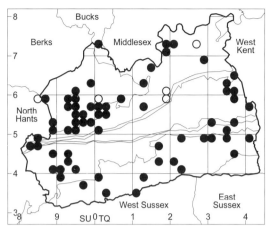

Haliplus sibiricus

Motschulsky, 1860

(= ***wehnckei*** Gerhardt, 1877)

Local in larger ponds, and among river- and canal-side vegetation. It is characteristic of very open sparsely vegetated areas such as the open lakes on Chobham Common and chalk-fed waters such as Silent Pool.

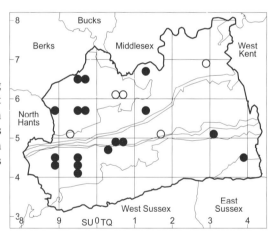

Haliplus variegatus Sturm, 1834

National Status: Rare (RDB3)

Extinct. Associated with shallow heathland pools and fens, still locally frequent in the New Forest.

RECORD – **Wandsworth**, <1856 (JAP).

NOTERIDAE – Burrowing Water Beetles

The two British species are distinctive, sleek-looking reddish-brown beetles. One is widespread and common, the other probably extinct in Surrey and nationally very local. The small antennae at once distinguish them from the diving beetles. The adults are primarily found in stagnant water, where they crawl around amongst the vegetation and litter. They are also good swimmers, adept at weaving around through submerged tangles. The biology is poorly known, as they spend a lot of time burrowing in the substrate.

Noterus clavicornis

(Degeer, 1774)   PLATE 10

The Larger Noterus

Widespread and abundant in ponds, especially those with abundant submerged vegetation and litter.

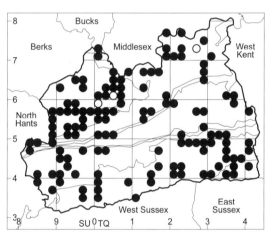

Noterus crassicornis

(Müller, O.F., 1776)   PLATE 10

The Smaller Noterus

Nationally Scarce B

Rare, possibly extinct. It occurs in fens, mires and ditches. Last recorded in 1944 on Esher Common.

RECORDS – **Wandsworth Common**, 1820 (A.Ingpen); **Putney Heath**, 1943 (JB-B); **Camberley**, 1943 (CET); **Black Pond, Esher**, 1944 (JB-B).

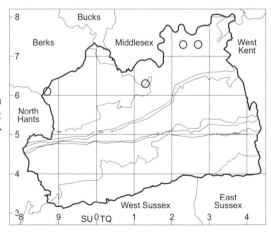

PAELOBIIDAE – Screech Beetles

Until recently known as Hygrobiidae, this small family has only seven species known worldwide, of which one, *Hygrobia hermanni*, occurs in Britain. The Screech Beetle is a very distinctive species, with equally distinctive larvae. It often announces its presence by stridulating in the pond net. The sound is made by rubbing the abdomen against a file of ridges on the inside of the elytra. These were once sold as novelties in Victorian markets, as they can be induced to 'squeak' when held between thumb and forefinger.

Hygrobia hermanni

(Fabricius, 1781)   PLATE 10

Screech Beetle

Widespread in ponds and small lakes, especially in ponds with soft silty substrates, where its larvae feed on *Tubifex* worms. In recent years I have taken it in large numbers in submerged *Sphagnum* at margins of very acidic heathland lakes. Whether it breeds in such sites is unclear.

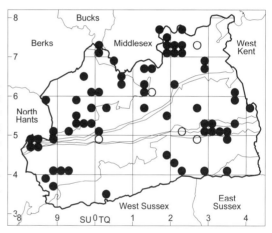

DYTISCIDAE – Diving Beetles

A diverse family which, with a few exceptions (*Hyphydrus* and *Hydrovatus*), have streamlined body-forms. All have the distinctive habit of regularly rising to the surface film 'tail first' and renewing the reservoir of air held beneath the wing-cases. The end of this reservoir appears as a bubble at the tip of the abdomen. The larvae are all carnivorous, and voracious. The common Great Diving Beetle has larvae which specialise in preying on amphibian tadpoles.

All move onto land to pupate, and the pupal cell is usually built under a stone or log (sometimes actually under the loose bark of fallen damp logs) close to the pond's edge. Soil is shaped to form a protective wall around the chamber in which the pupa will remain naked as it develops. 116 species have been recorded from the British Isles.

Agabus affinis

(Paykull, 1798)   PLATE 11

Very local in acid bog pools, usually amongst flooded *Sphagnum* on Lower Greensand and Thames basin heaths. It occasionally occurs in richer sites, including fens.

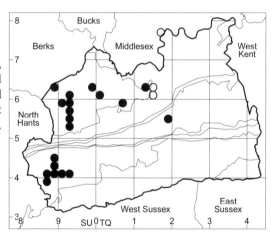

Agabus biguttatus (Olivier, 1795)

Nationally Scarce B

Rare, possibly extinct in Surrey. A semi-subterranean species associated with springs and well-head pools, especially in base-rich waters. The only county record was made at **Chiddingfold** in 1912 by W.E.Sharp. It was also recorded just over the county boundary on the Sussex parts of **Blackdown** by Frank Balfour-Browne and may await rediscovery.

Agabus bipustulatus

(Linnaeus, 1767)   PLATE 11

A strong flier which is ubiquitous in stagnant waters, being frequent in horse troughs and open water butts. Also frequently attracted to light and prone to landing on wet shiny black surfaces, which it presumably mistakes as water.

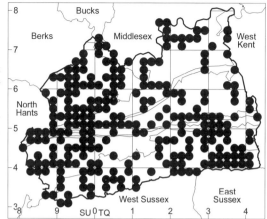

Agabus didymus

(Olivier, 1795)   PLATE 11

Widespread in streams and rivers, often amongst submerged vegetation, but avoiding areas with a strong current. Also frequents base-rich flowing water in bogs, as at Thursley NNR. Occasionally found in still water, and may breed in weedy ponds.

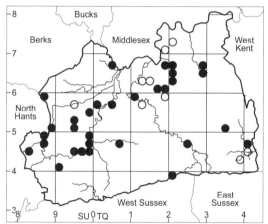

Agabus guttatus

(Paykull, 1798)   PLATE 11

Locally abundant at heads of natural springs, including acidic seepages in carr woodland. Also at outflows of land drains. Tolerant of shading and some pollution. Its prevalence at the boundaries of the underlying rock formations is clear.

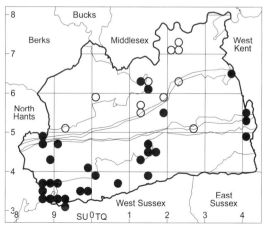

Agabus labiatus

(Brahm, 1790)   PLATE 11

Nationally Scarce B

A very local species of ephemeral heathland pools, where it is often abundant, especially in early spring.

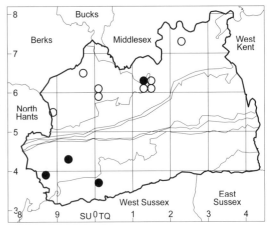

RECORDS – **Wimbledon**, 1890 (JAP); **Woking**, 1900 (WES); **Chobham**, 1900 (THB); **Claygate**, 1900 (WES); **Horsell Common**, 1906 (ECB), 4.1938 (FJC); **Oxshott**, 1931 (JLH); **Mytchett**, 1943 (EAD); **Dunsfold**, 1976 (JAO); **West End Common, Esher**, 1984 (JAO); **Churt Flashes**, 4-5.1998 (JSD); **Royal Common**, 27.4.2002 (JSD).

Agabus melanarius

Aubé, 1837

Nationally Scarce B

Very local but easily overlooked in shallow water amongst leaf litter and moss, primarily in boggy spring-fed areas of woodlands, but also in stagnant woodland pools. Also taken in a tiny leaf-choked, heavily shaded, butyl-lined garden pond at Crossways.

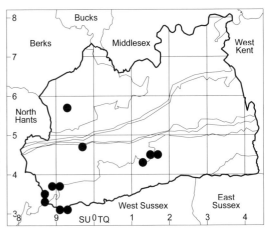

RECORDS – **Leith Hill**, 1978 (JAO), 9.2002 (JSD); **Pirbright Ranges**, 1990 (ITE); **Devil's Punchbowl**, 1994; **Whitmoor Vale**, 9.2000; **Hammer Bottom**, 3.2000; **Home Wood**, 22.2.2001; **Great Foxmoor Wood**, 2001; **Crossways, Hindhead**, 6.9.2002; **Redlands Wood**, 3.2002; **Boundless Copse**, 5.2002; **Bummoor Copse**, 10.2003 (JSD).

Agabus nebulosus

(Forster, 1771)   PLATE 11

This beautiful species is widespread but, as a breeder, somewhat localised to sparsely vegetated silt ponds. It is a rapid coloniser of new sites or ephemeral ponds on silt. Also regularly found in horse troughs.

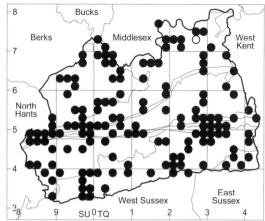

Agabus paludosus

(Fabricius, 1801)   PLATE 11

Another lovely insect, with translucent bases to its wing-cases. It is local in larger streams and rivers, especially on the chalk. It can also occur in shaded acidic seepages. It is often to be found amongst rafts of vegetation, such as watercress, in swift-flowing but shallow water.

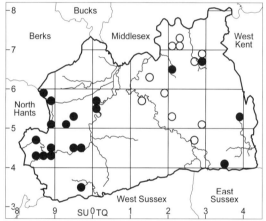

Agabus sturmii

(Gyllenhal, 1808)   PLATE 11

Widespread and often abundant in ponds and riverside situations with detritus. Adults become active in late winter or early spring.

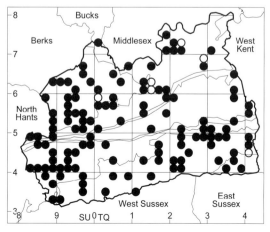

Agabus unguicularis

(Thomson, 1867)

Rare in ephemeral mesotrophic pools, in less acidic sites than *A. affinis*.

RECORDS – **Oxshott**, 1904; **Claygate**, 1906 (ECB); **Woking**, 1927 (CET); **Black Pond, Esher**, 1944 (JB-B); **Arbrook Common**, 1944 (JB-B); **Chobham Common**, 1986 (RBA).

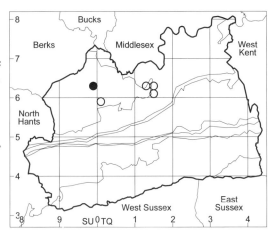

Ilybius aenescens

Thomson., C.G., 1870   PLATE 12

Nationally Scarce B

Rare on heathland in flooded *Sphagnum* in peat pools and at margins of large ponds.

RECORDS – **Claygate**, 1904 (ECB); **Oxshott**, 1940 (CET); **Black Pond, Esher**, 1976 (JAO), 2002 (JSD); **Thursley Common NNR**, 1999; **Moat Pond, Thursley**, in small mire at margins of open lake, 5.1990-2005; **Churt Flashes**, 5.1998; **Peatmoor Pond, Henley Park**, 4.1998; **Folly Bog**, 2000; **Pirbright Ranges**, 2003 (JSD).

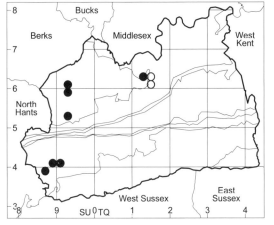

Ilybius ater

(Degeer, 1774)   PLATE 12

The Mud-dweller

The inappropriately named 'Mud-dweller' is our largest all black diving beetle, being 13-15mm long with the typical half-tear-drop-shaped profile. Widespread and fairly common in detritus pools, often in sites which occasionally dry out. Not infrequently taken at light.

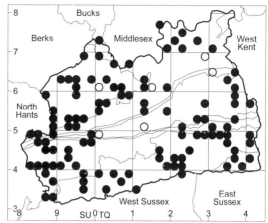

Ilybius chalconatus

(Panzer, 1796)

Nationally Scarce B

A local species found in woodland pools, and occasionally in ponds on open heaths. It is a common species in wheel-rut pools in clayey woodland.

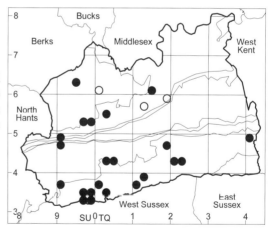

Ilybius fenestratus

(Fabricius, 1781)   PLATE 12

Nationally Scarce B

This species is often first noticed in the net by its distinctive (diagnostic) smell. Local but often abundant in larger permanent heathland ponds. Also found in the Basingstoke Canal, and old gravel pit lakes. It is unusual amongst the larger Dytiscids in surviving in numbers in waters heavily stocked with coarse fish. This species is strongly attracted (especially when teneral) to partly submerged weed tangles thrown up by wave-wash in reed beds around lakes.

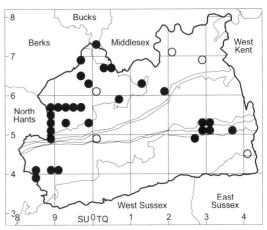

Ilybius fuliginosus

(Fabricius, 1792)   PLATE 12

Common in detritus ponds and in submerged vegetation at the edges of streams and rivers. This species is regularly taken at light.

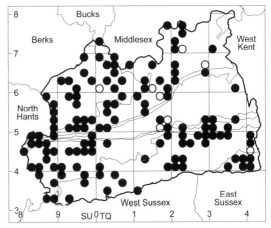

Ilybius guttiger

(Gyllenhal, 1808)   PLATE 12

Nationally Scarce B

A scarce species confined to pools in bogs, and swampy woodland sites, but avoiding deep shade.

RECORDS – **Hankley Common**, 1980 (JAO); **Gatton Park**, 1990 (APF); **Thursley Common NNR**, 1980 (JAO), 1998 (JSD); **Chobham Common**, 1986 (RBA), 1998 (JSD); **Peatmoor Pond, Henley Park**, 4.1998; **Greatbottom Flash**, 2000; **Thundry Meadows**, 30.4.2005; **Mill Lane, Godalming**, 25.5.2007 (JSD).

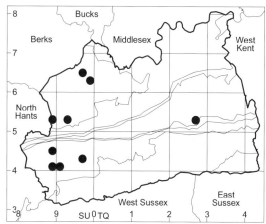

Ilybius montanus

Zimmermann, 1915

(formerly *Agabus melanocornis*)

PLATE 12

Local but often abundant, mainly in acidic ponds, primarily on heathland. It is often exceedingly numerous in open peat pools seemingly devoid of anything else!

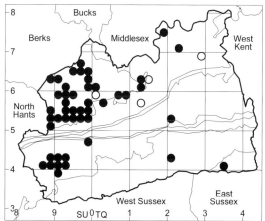

Ilybius quadriguttatus

(Lacordaire & Boisduval, 1835)

(= *obscurus* (Marsham))   PLATE 12

Very local in weedy ponds and ditches, and at lake edges, preferring base-rich conditions. It is rare or absent from acidic waters on heathland.

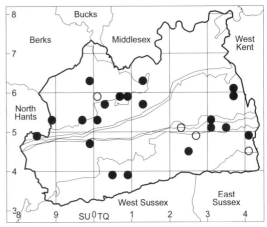

Ilybius subaeneus Erichson, 1837

Nationally Scarce B

Rare, possibly extinct in Surrey. It was recorded at **Peckham** in the early 19th Century. It was in Woolmer Pond in North Hampshire up to the mid 1970s, but is now lost from here also.

Platambus maculatus

(Linnaeus, 1758)   PLATE 11

This beautifully marked beetle is widespread throughout much of rural Surrey. It occurs in streams and at river edges, in both open and shaded situations.

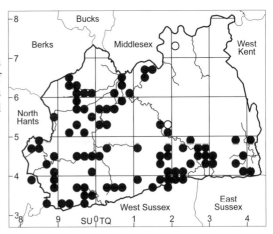

DENSITY OF STREAMS AND PONDS IN SURREY

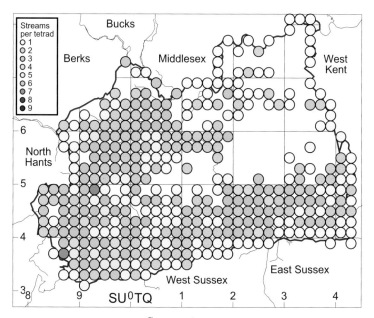

Surrey streams

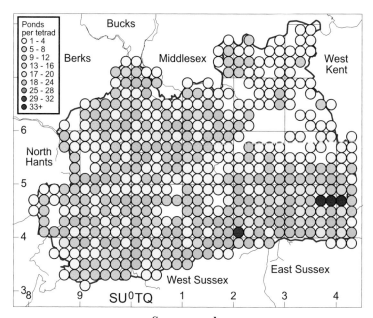

Surrey ponds

PLATE 1

All photographs are the copyright of the author, with the exception of three:
Plate 21 *Hygrotus nigrolineatus* copyright Franz Hebauer, and
Laccornis oblongus copyright Geoff Nobes;
Plate 25 *Hydrophilus piceus* copyright Paul Sterry.

In the captions, figures in brackets refer to length.

NEPIDAE – Water Scorpions

Water Scorpion *Nepa cinerea* – left, nymph (12mm); right, adult dorsal (17-23mm);
below, adult front view

PLATE 2

NEPIDAE (continued)

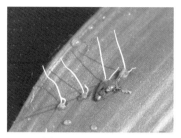 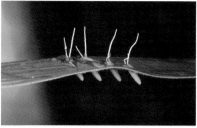

Water Stick-insect *Ranatra linearis* eggs laid in floating leaf of broad-leaved pondweed

Can you see me?

Water Stick-insect *Ranatra linearis* (30-35mm)

PLATE 3

CORIXIDAE

Micronecta nymph (2mm)

Micronecta scholtzi adult
(2.5mm)

Corixa punctata – left, nymph; right, adult (12-14mm)

Sigara limitata (5-6.5mm)

Hesperocorixa castanea (5mm)

Cymatia bonsdorffii (5.5-6.5mm)

Cymatia coleoptrata
(3-4.5mm)

PLATE 4

NAUCORIDAE

APHELOCHEIRIDAE

Saucer Bug *Ilyocoris cimicoides*
(11-15mm)

River Saucer Bug *Aphelocheirus aestivalis* (8-10mm)

NOTONECTIDAE – Water-boatmen, Backswimmers

Common Water-boatman *Notonecta glauca* – left, nymph; right, adult on land
(14-16mm)

Peppered Water-boatman *Notonecta maculata*
(14-16mm)

Pied Water-boatman *Notonecta obliqua* (14-16mm)

PLATE 5

PLEIDAE

Least Water-boatman *Plea minutissima* (2mm)

MESOVELIIDAE

HEBRIDAE – Velvet Water Bugs

Pondweed Bug *Mesovelia furcata* – left, nymph; right, adult (3.5mm)

Sphagnum Bug *Hebrus ruficeps* (1.4mm)

HYDROMETRIDAE – Water Measurers

Water Measurer *Hydrometra stagnorum* – left, adult (9-12mm); right, a rare winged adult

PLATE 6

VELIIDAE – Water-crickets

Minute Water-cricket *Microvelia reticulata* (1.4mm)

Microvelia pygmaea (1.3mm)

Water-cricket *Velia caprai* – left, nymph; right, adult female, wingless (6-8mm)

GERRIDAE – Pondskaters, Water-striders

Common Pondskater *Gerris lacustris* (8-10mm)

Gerris lateralis (9-11mm)

PLATE 7

GERRIDAE (continued)

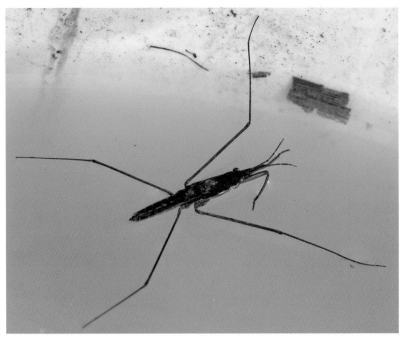

River Pondskater *Aquarius najas* (15mm)

SALDIDAE – Shore Bugs

**CICADELLIDAE –
Leaf-hoppers**

Chartoscirta cincta (3.8mm)

Common Shore Bug
Saldula saltatoria (4.5mm)

Pondweed Hopper
Macrosteles cyane (4.5mm)

PLATE 8

GYRINIDAE – Whirlygig Beetles

Common Whirlygigs *Gyrinus substriatus* (5-7mm)

The Artist *Gyrinus urinator* – above, larva;
below, adult (5-7mm)

Hairy Whirlygig *Orectochilus villosus*
(5.5-6.5mm)

HALIPLIDAE – Crawling Water Beetles

Brychius elevatus
(3.5-4mm)

Peltodytes caesus (3.5-4mm)

Haliplus flavicollis (3.8mm)

PLATE 9

HALIPLIDAE (continued)

Haliplus obliquus
(3.2mm)

Haliplus lineatocollis
(3mm)

Haliplus ruficollis
(2.5-3mm)

NOTERIDAE – Burrowing Water Beetles

The Larger Noterus *Noterus
clavicornis* (4-5mm)

The Smaller Noterus
Noterus crassicornis
(3.5-4mm)

PAELOBIIDAE – Screech Beetles

Screech Beetle *Hygrobia hermanni* – left, larva; right, adult (8.5-10mm)

PLATE 10

DYTISCIDAE – Diving Beetles – *Agabus, Platambus*

Agabus affinis (6mm)

Agabus bipustulatus – left, larva; right, adult (11mm)

Flowing water species

Platambus maculatus
(7.5mm)

Agabus didymus
(7.5mm)

Agabus paludosus
(7mm)

Agabus guttatus
(8.5mm)

Agabus labiatus (6mm)

Agabus nebulosus (8mm)

Agabus sturmii
(8mm)

Agabus undulatus
(non-Surrey) (8mm)

PLATE 11

DYTISCIDAE (continued) – *Ilybius*

Ilybius montanus (6-8mm)

Ilybius aenescens (9mm)   *Ilybius guttiger* (9.5mm)

Ilybius fuliginosus (11mm)   *Ilybius fenestratus* (11.5mm)

Ilybius quadriguttatus (11mm)

The Mud-dweller *Ilybius ater*
(13-15mm)

PLATE 12

DYTISCIDAE (continued) – *Colymbetes, Rhantus*

Colymbetes fuscus – left, larva; right, adult (16-18mm)

Rhantus exsoletus (9-10mm)

Rhantus grapii (10-11mm)

PLATE 13

DYTISCIDAE (continued) – *Rhantus, Liopterus*

Rhantus frontalis (10-11mm); right, female underside

Rhantus suturalis (10-12mm); right, underside

Piles Beetle *Liopterus haemorrhoidalis* (7-8mm)

PLATE 14

DYTISCIDAE (continued) – *Acilius, Graphoderus*

Acilius sulcatus – left, larva; right, adult male and female (16-18mm)

Acilius canaliculatus female
(14mm)

Graphoderus cinereus (13-16mm)

PLATE 15

DYTISCIDAE (continued) – *Dytiscus*

Dytiscus circumflexus (26-32mm) – above, female dorsal;
below, female underside

PLATE 16

DYTISCIDAE (continued) – *Dytiscus*

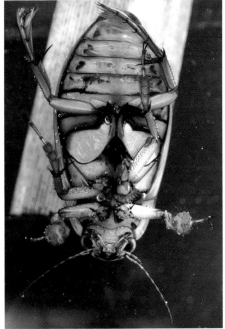

Great Diving Beetle *Dytiscus marginalis*
(26-32mm) – above, male dorsal; below, male
underside (note the sucker cups on the front legs)

PLATE 17

DYTISCIDAE (continued) – Life cycle of a Diving Beetle *Dytiscus semisulcatus*

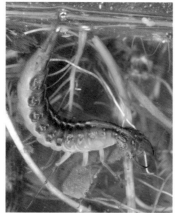

Larva

Larva excavating pupal cell

Pupa

Teneral adult

Adult female (25mm)

PLATE 18

DYTISCIDAE (continued) – *Hydaticus,* smaller Dytiscids

Hydaticus seminiger (13-14.5mm)　　　*Hydaticus transversalis* (13mm)

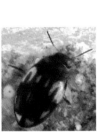   

Hydroglyphus pusillus　　*Deronectes latus*　　*Graptodytes*　　*Graptodytes pictus*
(2mm)　　　　　　　(4.5mm)　　　*granularis* (2.2mm)　　(2.2mm)

Hydroporus　　　　*Hydroporus*　　*Hydroporus gyllenhalii*　　*Hydroporus*
angustatus　　　*erythrocephalus*　　　(4mm)　　　　*incognitus*
(3mm)　　　　　　(4mm)　　　　　　　　　　　　(3.5mm)

PLATE 19

DYTISCIDAE (continued)

Hydroporus melan-arius (3-3.5mm)   *Hydroporus memnonius* (4mm)   *Hydroporus neglectus* (2.5mm)   *Hydroporus palustris* (3.3-3.8mm)

Hydroporus planus (4.5mm)   *Hydroporus striola* (3-3.4mm)   *Hydroporus tessellatus* (3.5mm)   *Porhydrus lineatus* (3mm)

Stictonectes lepidus (3mm)   *Oreodytes sanmarki* (3mm) light and dark forms   *Hydrovatus clypealis* (2-2.3mm)

Suphrodytes dorsalis (5mm)   *Nebrioporus elegans* (4.5-5mm) light and dark forms   *Stictotarsus duodecim-pustulatus* (6mm)

PLATE 20

DYTISCIDAE (continued)

Hygrotus confluens (3mm)	*Hygrotus nigrolineatus* (3mm)	*Hygrotus decoratus* (2mm)	*Hygrotus inaequalis* (3mm)

Hygrotus impresso-punctatus (5mm)	*Hygrotus parallelogrammus* (5mm)	*Hygrotus versicolor* (4mm)

Hyphydrus ovatus (4.5-5mm)	*Laccornis oblongus* (5mm)	*Laccophilus hyalinus* (4-4.5mm)	*Laccophilus minutus* (4-4.5mm)

HYDRAENIDAE

Hydraena riparia (2-2.5mm)	*Ochthebius minimus* (1.5-2mm)	*Limnebius truncatellus* (2mm)

PLATE 21

HELOPHORIDAE

Helophorus aequalis
(4.5-6.5mm)

Helophorus grandis
(5.5-7mm)

Helophorus dorsalis
(3-4mm)

GEORISSIDAE – Mud-coater Beetles

Georissus crenulatus (1.5-1.8mm) –
left, cleaned; right, half coated!

HYDROCHIDAE

Hydrochus angustatus (3-4mm)

Hydrochus elongatus
(3-4.5mm)

PLATE 22

HYDROPHILIDAE – Water Scavenger Beetles

Berosus affinis (5mm)   *Berosus signaticollis* (5.5mm)   *Chaetarthria simillima* (1.5mm)

Paracymus scutellaris (3mm)   *Anacaena bipustulata* (2mm)   *Anacaena limbata* (2.5-3mm)   *Anacaena globulus* (2.5-3mm)

Laccobius bipunctatus (3.5-4mm)   *Helochares punctatus* (4.5-6.5mm) with egg cocoon

PLATE 23

HYDROPHILIDAE (continued)

Enochrus coarctatus
(3.5-4.6mm)

Enochrus ochropterus
(5mm)

Enochrus testaceus
(6-7mm)

Hydrobius fuscipes (5-8mm) – right, showing air reserves on underside

Cymbiodyta marginellus
(4-4.5mm)

Coelostoma orbiculare
(4.5-5mm)

Cercyon marinus
(2.5-3mm)

PLATE 24

HYDROPHILIDAE (continued)

Lesser Silver Water Beetle *Hydrochara caraboides*
(14-18mm)

Great Silver Water Beetle *Hydrophilus piceus* (34-37mm)

ELMIDAE – Riffle Beetles

Elmis aenea larva
(2.5mm)

Left, *Limnius volckmari* (2.9-3.2mm)
Right, *Elmis aenea* (1.9-2.2mm)

Oulimnius tuberculatus (1.8mm)

PLATE 25

SCIRTIDAE – Marsh Beetles

Elodes minuta (4-6mm) with wings extended

Microcara testacea (4.5-5.5mm)

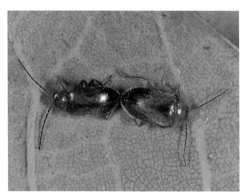

Elodes elongata (5mm) *in copula*

Odeles marginata (5.5mm)

Cyphon padi
(3-4mm)

Cyphon variabilis
(3.5mm)

The Tree-hole
Beetle
*Prionocyphon
serricornis*
(3.5-4mm)

Scirtes orbicularis
(3.5mm)

PLATE 26

SCIRTIDAE – Marsh Beetles – larvae

Elodes *Scirtes hemisphaericus* *Microcara testacea* *Cyphon*

The Tree-hole Beetle *Prionocyphon serricornis* –
left, root pool in beech tree; right, larvae among beech leaves

DRYOPIDAE – Hairy Crawling Water Beetles

HETEROCERIDAE – Burrowing Mud Beetles

Dryops luridus *Dryops striatellus* *Pomatinus substriatus*
(4.5mm)　　　(3.5mm)　　　(5mm)

Heterocerus fenestratus
(3.5-4mm)

PLATE 27

CHRYSOMELIDAE – Leaf Beetles

Golden Reed Beetle
Donacia bicolora (10mm)

Hairy Reed Beetle
Donacia cinerea (9mm)

Yellow-legged Reed Beetle
Donacia clavipes (11mm)

Donacia impressa (9mm)

Donacia marginata (9mm)

Donacia simplex (9mm)

Water-lily Reed Beetle *Donacia crassipes*
(11mm)

Donacia versicolorea (10mm)

PLATE 28

CHRYSOMELIDAE (continued)

Plateumaris affinis (7mm)   *Plateumaris sericea* (7mm)

Donacia vulgaris (9mm) – below, larva attached to reedmace roots

Galerucella sagittariae (5mm), female with eggs on amphibious bistort

Galerucella nymphaeae (5.5mm) – right, mating on water-lilies   *Galerucella calmariensis* (4mm)

PLATE 29

AQUATIC WEEVILS

NANOPHYIDAE

Dieckmanniellus gracilis (2mm)

ERIRHINIDAE

| Horsetail Weevil
Grypus equiseti
(5.5-6.5mm) | *Notaris acridulus*
(3.5-5mm) | *Notaris scirpi*
(6-7.5mm) | *Thryogenes nereis*
(3.5-4mm) |

Azolla Weevil *Stenopelmus rufinasus* (2mm) – right, on host plant

PLATE 30

CURCULIONIDAE

Gymnetron beccabungae
(2.3mm)

Gymnetron veronicae
(2.3mm)

*Gymnetron
villosulum*
(2.5-3mm) *in copula*

Water Plantain Weevil
Bagous alismatis
(3mm)

Bagous limosus
(3mm)

Bagous lutulentus
(3.5mm)

Bagous tempestivus
(3mm)

Duckweed Weevil
Tanysphyrus lemnae
(1.5mm)

Eubrychius velutus
(2.5mm)

Drupenatus nasturtii
(3-3.5mm)

Poophagus sisymbrii
(3-3.5mm)

Lixus paraplecticus (15mm)

PLATE 31

CURCULIONIDAE (continued)

Limnobaris dolorosa
(3.5mm)

Limnobaris t-album
(3.5mm)

Yellow Loosestrife Weevil
Tapeinotus sellatus (3.5-4mm)

Pelonomus comari
(3mm)

Phytobius leucogaster
(3.5mm)

Rhinoncus albicinctus
(3mm)

CARABIDAE – Ground Beetles

Swimming Ground Beetle *Oodes helopioides* (8mm)

PLATE 32

Colymbetes fuscus

(Linnaeus, 1758)   PLATE 13

Common, in a variety of still water habitats. Also comes to light, especially when teneral.

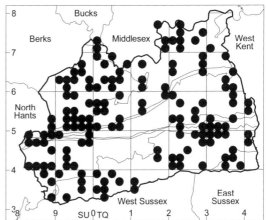

Rhantus exsoletus

(Forster, 1771)   PLATE 13

Local in a variety of ponds, especially on heathland. I took a singleton in weed at the margins of the River Blackwater at **Hawley Meadows** in 2000. Also in old sandpits as at **Papercourt** marshes.

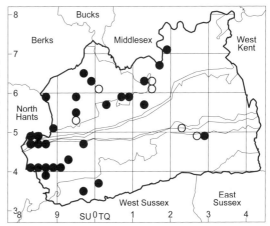

Rhantus frontalis

(Marsham, 1802)   PLATE 14

Nationally Scarce B

Rare in Surrey in old detritus ponds.

RECORDS – **Wandsworth Common**, 1829 (JFS); **Reigate Heath**, 1856; **Earlswood**, 1856 (JL); **Dunsfold**, 1976 (JAO).

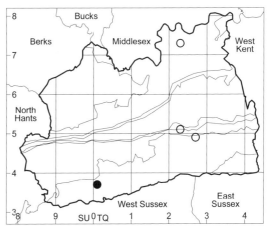

Rhantus grapii

(Gyllenhal, 1808)   PLATE 13

Nationally Scarce B

Local. Can be abundant at margins of detritus ponds living amongst rafts of submerged moss, including *Sphagnum* and *Drepanocladus*, or grass such as *Glyceria fluitans*. Locally frequent in old field ponds on the Weald Clay.

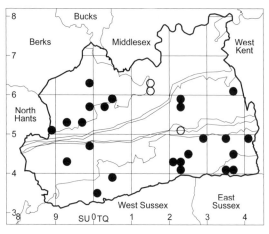

Rhantus suturalis

(Macleay, 1825)   PLATE 14

Nationally Scarce B

Very local in silt and detritus pools. It is a strong flier which could turn up virtually anywhere and is not infrequently taken at light, especially when teneral.

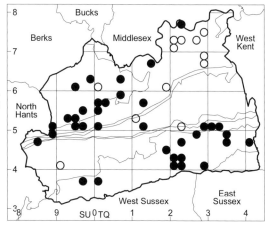

Rhantus suturellus

(Harris, T.W., 1828)

Locally abundant in heathland pools, including bog pools over peat.

RECORDS – **Woking**, 1888 (AJC); **Horsell Common**, 1906 (ECB); **Oxshott**, 1940 (CET); **Wisley Common**, 1980 (JAO), 2000 (JSD); **Wimbledon Common**, 1982 (APF); **Peatmoor Pond, Henley Park, & Whitepatch Bottom**, 4.1998 (JSD); **Moat Pond, Thursley, & Thursley Common**, various peat pools on open bog system, 5.1998 (JSD); **Churt Flashes**, 5.1998 (JSD); **Chobham Common**, 1976 (JAO), on NNR, 8.1999 (JSD); **Broomhall Heath**, 8.2000; **Strawberry Bottom**, 24.7.2003 (JSD).

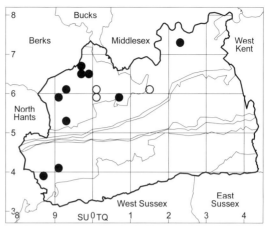

Liopterus haemorrhoidalis

(Fabricius, 1787)   PLATE 14

Piles Beetle

Until recently known as *Copelatus haemorrhoidalis*, the Piles Beetle is a local species of detritus ponds and bog pools. Often to be found in old field and village ponds.

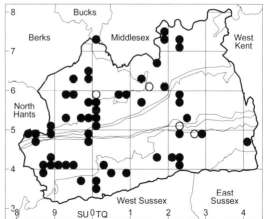

Acilius canaliculatus (Nicolai, 1822)   PLATE 15

National Status: Rare (RDB3)

Extinct. Found in shaded leaf-filled ephemeral pools in woodland in Kent, where it was discovered as recently as the 1980s. Found in the Reigate area by J.Linnell in the mid 19th Century; there have been no records since, but it may await rediscovery in Surrey.

Acilius sulcatus

(Linnaeus, 1758)   PLATE 15

Local in fish-free ponds and pools with open sections where the free-swimming larvae forage. Tolerant of heavy shading. Often diurnally active, and conspicuous as it swims in open water.

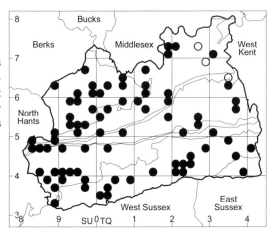

Graphoderus cinereus

(Linnaeus, 1758)   PLATE 15

National Status: Rare (RDB3)

Unfortunately this beautiful beetle is a great rarity in Britain. It is associated with fish-free ponds and ditches. The larvae are free-swimming, feeding on cladocerans, etc., in open water.

RECORDS – **Black Pond, Esher**, 1970s (JAO); **Bookham Common**, in weedy pond, 19.8.1984 (Ron Carr).

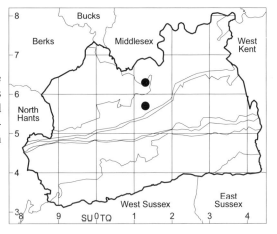

Dytiscus circumcinctus Ahrens, 1811

Nationally Scarce B

Associated with well-vegetated ponds and ditches, and most frequent in areas with abundant long-established water bodies, as on the Cheshire Plain.

RECORD – **Richmond Park**, circa 1900 (HSD).

Dytiscus circumflexus

Fabricius, 1801   PLATE 16

Nationally Scarce B

Easily identified by its wasp-banded underside, and greenish sheen to the upperside. It is very local and primarily coastal, often in slightly brackish ditches, but inland in large heathland ponds. In recent years it has cropped up in newly cleared ponds with exposed silt substrates.

RECORDS – **Battersea Fields**, 1829 (JFS); **Redhill**, 1853 (JL); **Richmond Park**, 1900 (HSD); **Kew Gardens**, 1910 (WES); **Mitcham**, 1953 (LC); **Moat Pond, Thursley**, 1978 (JAO); **Farnham Park**, 1998-9 (JSD).

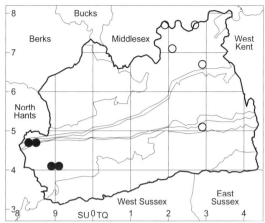

Dytiscus dimidiatus Bergsträsser, 1778

King Diving Beetle

National Status: Rare (RDB3)

Probably extinct in Surrey, Britain's largest carnivorous beetle is a spectacular inhabitant of marsh dykes, fen pools and richly vegetated ponds. The only record from Surrey is from **Merton** in 1896 (E.A.Newbery).

Dytiscus marginalis

Linnaeus, 1758   PLATE 17

Great Diving Beetle

Perhaps the most familiar of water beetles, this large and spectacular insect is widespread and common in stagnant water. Its ferocious-looking larvae are voracious predators, primarily of tadpoles, especially those of frogs and toads.

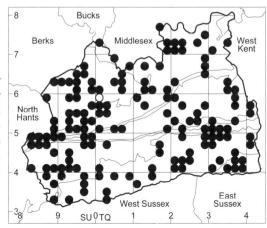

Dytiscus semisulcatus

Müller, O.F., 1776   PLATE 18

The only black-bellied *Dytiscus* is a local species, rarely found away from heathland ponds. The larvae, which develop through the winter months, are specialist predators of caddis larvae.

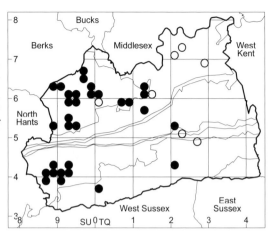

Hydaticus seminiger

(Degeer, 1774)   PLATE 19

Nationally Scarce B

This distinctive species, 13 to 14.5mm long, is local but has been increasingly frequent over the past decade or so. Often in shaded detritus pools, but also in flooded *Sphagnum* and other dense submerged vegetation in open situations.

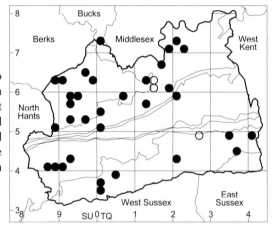

Hydaticus transversalis (Pontoppidan, 1763)   PLATE 19

National Status: Rare (RDB3)

Extinct in Surrey. This handsome insect was found in the Thames Marshes in the mid 19th Century, but today its strongholds are in the Somerset levels and Norfolk Broads.

Hydroglyphus pusillus

(Fabricius, 1781)   PLATE 19

Nationally Scarce B

Local in silty ponds and sand pits, including large puddles devoid of vegetation, but fading out as these become well vegetated.

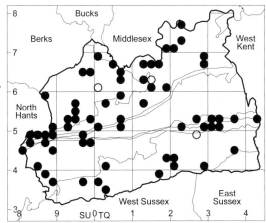

Deronectes latus (Stephens, 1829)   PLATE 19

Nationally Scarce B

This distinctive denizen of swift-flowing water is amongst the most elusive of Dytiscids and is easily overlooked in its haunts in dark shady overhangs. It is usually in streams devoid of vegetation, often in dense shade. It also occurs under bridges.

RECORDS – Sub-fossil remains found in the Thames at **Runnymede** date to the Bronze Age (Robinson, 1991). I took it in the **R.Wey**, near **Dockenfield**, in 10.2006 (JSD).

Graptodytes flavipes

(Olivier, 1795)

National Status: Vulnerable (RDB2)

Rare, possibly extinct in Surrey. It occurs in shallow water in poor fens and heath pools. Last recorded at Bookham Common in 1965.

RECORDS – **Reigate Heath**, c.1851; **Earlswood**, c.1851 (JL); **Esher & Oxshott**, 1900 (HSD); **Claygate**, 1902 (ECB); **Horsell Common**, 1906 (ECB); **Woking**, 1909 (FB-B); **Walton Heath**, 1926? (JLH); **Bookham Common**, 1965 (JC).

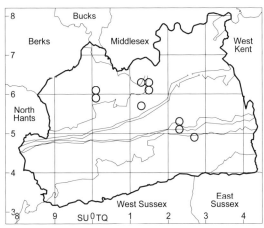

Graptodytes granularis

(Linnaeus, 1767)   PLATE 19

Nationally Scarce B

Rare in shallow richly-vegetated fen habitats, including weed-choked ponds as at West End Common, Esher.

RECORDS – **Wimbledon**, 1900 (WES); **Bookham Common**, 1907 (EEB); **Woking**, 1908 (AJC); **Horsell Common & Woking**, 1909 (FB-B); **Wisley**, 1920; **Oxshott**, 1927 (JLH); **Arbrook Common**, 1946 (JB-B); **Thursley Common**, 1967 (GNF); **Ockham**, 1977 (PJH); **Teal Pond, Wisley**, 1983 (APF); **West End Common, Esher**, 1980 (JAO), 2002 (JSD).

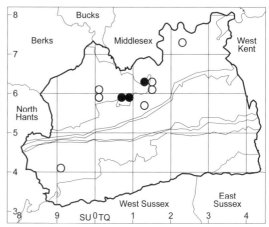

Graptodytes pictus

(Fabricius, 1787)   PLATE 19

Another surprisingly rare species in Surrey. It resides in weedy ponds and especially in marsh dykes and ditches. Last recorded by John Owen in the 1970s in TQ16.

RECORDS – **Earlswood**, <1851 (JL); **Wray Common**, 1853; **Sidlow Bridge**, 1853 (JL); **Woking**, 1887 (GCC); **Beverley Brook, Richmond Park**, 1900 (THB), **Oxshott**, 1920 (HSD); **Wisley**, 1920 (JLH); **Bookham Common**, 1932 (FJC); **Epsom Common**, 1952 (LC), 1976 (JAO).

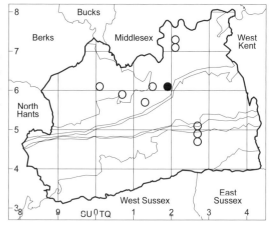

Genus *Hydroporus*

This is the most species-rich Dytiscid genus in Britain, and most of them have occurred in Surrey. They are all small beetles, those present in Surrey ranging in size from 2.2 to 4.6mm.

Hydroporus angustatus

Sturm, 1835   PLATE 19

Widespread in detritus ponds, but absent from very acid sites. Tolerant of shading.

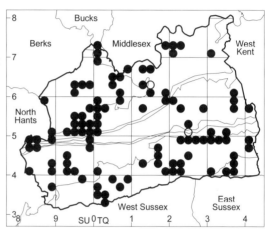

Hydroporus discretus

Fairmaire, 1859

A local species which breeds in small water bodies, such as spring-heads, and in still backwaters of streams. It is a frequent inhabitant of pools fed by ground water, but also lives in shady wheel-rut pools in clayey woodland areas. It is tolerant of shading.

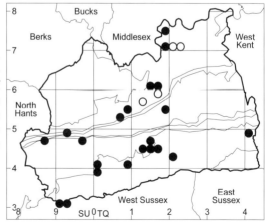

Hydroporus erythrocephalus

(Linnaeus, 1758)   PLATE 19

Local in ponds with detritus, especially on heathland, where it is a common species in *Sphagnum* pools and small water bodies in rush pasture and wet heath areas.

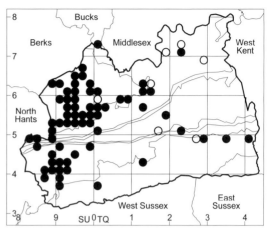

Hydroporus ferrugineus Stephens, 1829

Nationally Scarce B

A very localised species, associated with spring-heads and ground-water-fed seepages. In Surrey it appears to be restricted to the high ground around Leith Hill, and, despite several searches, appears to be absent from several equally suitable areas, including the Devil's Punchbowl, Hammer Bottom and Friday Street.

RECORDS – **Mitcham**, 9.1892 (HH); **Leith Hill**, 1978 (JAO); **Great Foxmore Wood, Broadmoor (Abinger)** & **Redlands Wood**, 2002 (JSD).

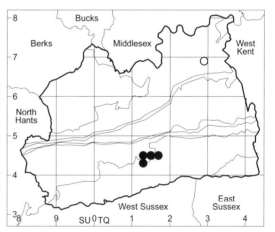

Hydroporus gyllenhalii

Schiødte, 1841   PLATE 19

Locally abundant in acid heathland ponds and bog sites, often amongst *Sphagnum* carpets, including partially shaded sites.

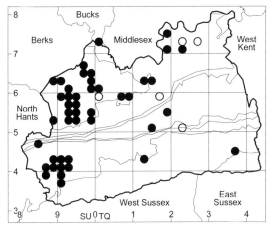

Hydroporus incognitus

Sharp, 1869   PLATE 19

Widespread, perhaps commonest in shaded water including acidic seepages, but it is also often to be found in calm waters at the margins of rivers, and occasionally in open field ponds.

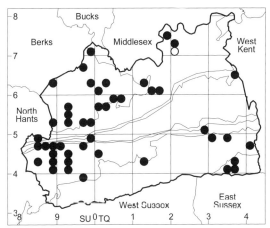

Hydroporus longulus

Mulsant, 1860

Nationally Scarce B

Very local in moss and leaves in spring-fed boggy ground. Also occasionally taken in debris in streams where it is presumably carried by flood water.

RECORDS – **Esher**, 1866 (JAP); **Surbiton**, 1866 (ECR); **Woking**, 1893 (AJC); **Holloway College**, 1980 (RBA); **Oyster Wood**, 1989 (JAO); **Devil's Punchbowl**, 3.1992; **Hazelbridge**, 4.92; **Whitmoor Vale**, 9.2000; **Hammer Bottom**, 2000; **Home Wood**, 3.2001; **Nore Hill**, 3.2002; **Boundless Copse**, 5.2002; **Chadhurst Moor**, 3.2002; **Bummoor Copse**, 10.2003; **Hambledon House**, 8.2006 (JSD).

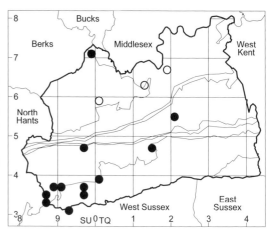

Hydroporus melanarius

Sturm, 1835   PLATE 20

A very local species confined to small pools, usually seasonal, on heathy sites. It also occurs in pools in rush pasture, often in the most meagre puddles. In Surrey it is much scarcer than 'Nationally Scarce' taxa such as *Hydroporus neglectus* and *Helochares punctatus*.

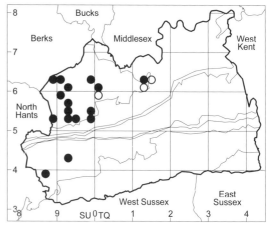

100

Hydroporus memnonius

Nicolai, 1822   PLATE 20

Widespread in shallow water over detritus. It is usually found in shaded woodland pools with abundant leaf litter, in which (with the exception of *Microcara testacea*) it is often the only water beetle present.

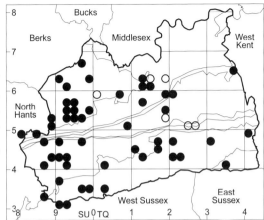

Hydroporus neglectus

Schaum, 1845   PLATE 20

Nationally Scarce B

Very local in shaded pools, usually amongst submerged leaf litter, or in *Sphagnum*. It does occasionally occur in more open pools, as on Whitmoor Common, but this is exceptional.

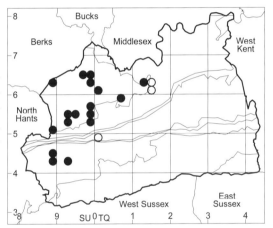

Hydroporus nigrita

(Fabricius, 1792)

Widespread but local in a variety of still and often sparsely vegetated waters, including wheel-rut pools, puddles and small detritus ponds.

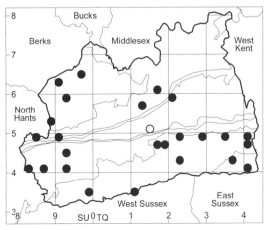

Hydroporus obscurus

Sturm, 1835

Very local and restricted to open areas of flooded *Sphagnum* in bogs and deeper heathland pools.

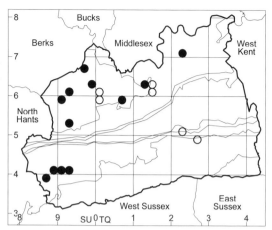

Hydroporus palustris

(Linnaeus, 1761)   PLATE 20

Common in stagnant detritus ponds and less commonly at edges of flowing water.

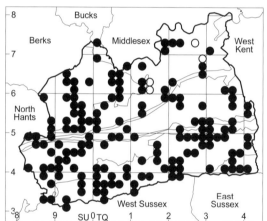

Hydroporus planus

(Fabricius, 1781)   PLATE 20

Widespread and common in still water habitats, especially temporary pools, and also frequent in cattle troughs.

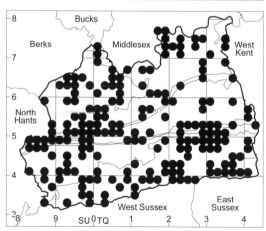

Hydroporus pubescens

(Gyllenhal, 1808)

Widespread and common, especially in ephemeral pools on heathland, but absent from chalky areas.

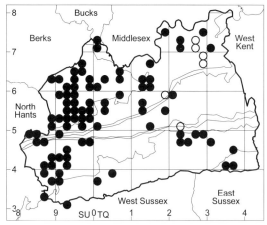

Hydroporus rufifrons (Müller, 1776)
Oxbow diving beetle

National Status: Vulnerable (RDB2)

Probably extinct. A rare and declining species of seasonally flooded wetlands, especially on flood-plains.

RECORD – **Chobham**, circa 1900 (GCC).

Hydroporus striola

(Gyllenhal, 1827)   PLATE 20

Locally abundant in ponds rich in detritus, often in shaded sites. Also occurs in *Sphagnum* at margins of heathland pools.

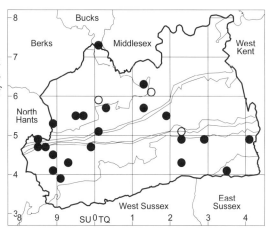

Hydroporus tessellatus

(Drapiez, 1819)   PLATE 20

Widespread and common. It is a strong flier which turns up in a wide range of sites, including puddles and water troughs, although it was represented by singletons at a large proportion of the sites mapped, and so the number of sites in which it actually breeds successfully is rather limited.

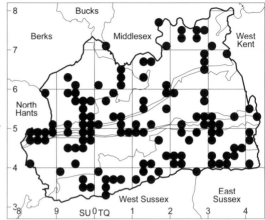

Hydroporus tristis

(Paykull, 1798)

Very local in detritus pools and amongst *Sphagnum* in bog pools, but also found in more open heath ponds, and often taken with *H. umbrosus*.

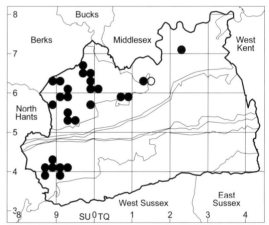

Hydroporus umbrosus

(Gyllenhal, 1808)

Very local in detritus pools and bogs, usually with some *Sphagnum,* but also found in more open heath ponds, and often taken with *H. tristis*.

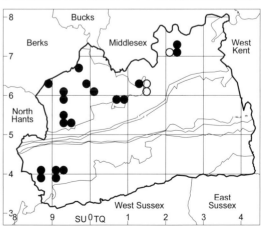

Nebrioporus assimilis (Paykull, 1798)

Extinct in southern England. Associated with ponds, drains and ditches.
Recorded from **Reigate Heath** by J.Linnell before 1866.

Nebrioporus elegans

(Panzer, 1794)   PLATE 20

Locally abundant in larger streams and rivers, especially on coarse substrates. I also found it in numbers in a deep, sparsely vegetated pond in a sand pit.

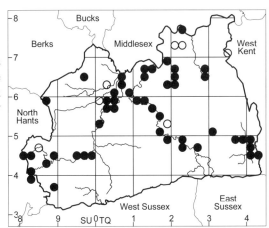

Oreodytes sanmarki

(Sahlberg, C.R., 1826)   PLATE 20

Very rare, restricted to swift-flowing streams with coarse substrates. Often found in root tangles, and tolerant of heavy shading. Primarily a northern and western species in Britain, largely as a result of the paucity of swift-flowing stony streams in the south-east, although it is widespread in North Hampshire.

RECORD – **Hammer Bottom**, 4.2000 (JSD).

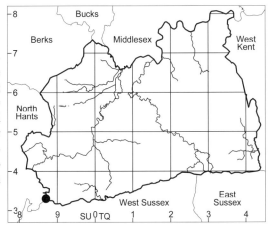

Porhydrus lineatus

(Fabricius, 1775)   PLATE 20

This distinctive beetle is surprisingly rare in Surrey (and North Hampshire), possibly as a result of the paucity of well-vegetated ditches. Foster (1972) notes that it is common in the coastal marshes but almost absent from inland parts of East Sussex, including the area shown on this map. It was last recorded by John Owen at Dunsfold in 1976.

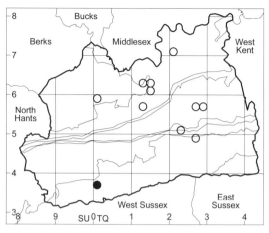

RECORDS – **Reigate Heath**, 1856; **Earlswood**, 1865 (JL); **Oxshott**, 1899 (AJC); **Richmond**, 1900 (THB); **Woking**, 1909 (FB-B); **Chipstead**, 1926 (JLH); **Esher Common**, 1932 (FJC); **Bookham Common**, 1940 (CET); **Arbrook Common**, 1946 (JB-B); **Dunsfold**, 1976 (JAO).

Stictonectes lepidus

(Olivier, 1795)   PLATE 20

Nationally Scarce B

Rare, possibly extinct in Surrey. Last recorded at Oxshott between 1897 and 1904 (HSD). It is usually found in ponds which have a through-flow, including dam ponds, and pools left as streams dry out.

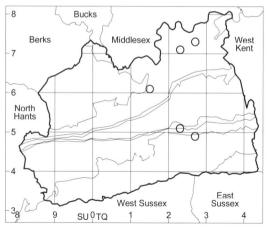

RECORDS – **Wandsworth Common**, 1820 (A.Ingpen); **Reigate Heath**, 1856 (JL); **Earlswood**, 1856 (JL); **Wimbledon Common**, 1868 (ECR); **Oxshott**, 1900 (HSD).

Stictotarsus duodecimpustulatus

(Fabricius, 1792)   PLATE 20

This handsome beetle is surprisingly scarce in Surrey, despite being recorded from most of the river systems. It resides in flowing water, especially in deep weed-free sections.

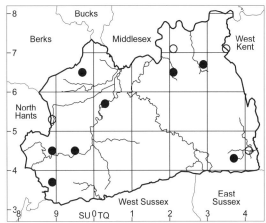

Suphrodytes dorsalis

(Fabricius, 1787)   PLATE 20

Very local in partly shaded detritus pools in both base-rich and acidic sites.

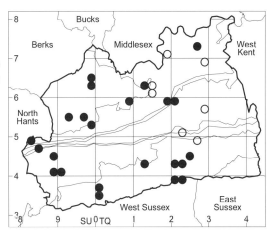

Hydrovatus clypealis Sharp, 1876   PLATE 20

Nationally Scarce B

Rare, possibly extinct in Surrey, this tiny Dytiscid was taken in **Richmond Park** in 1937 (Pearce, 1937).

Hygrotus confluens

(Fabricius, 1787)   PLATE 21

Very local in sparsely vegetated ponds, often with *Hydroglyphus pusillus*, but an efficient coloniser of new ponds, fading out as these become established and vegetated.

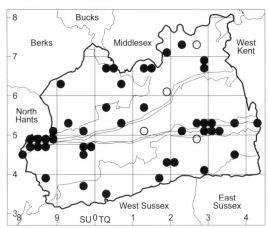

Hygrotus decoratus

(Gyllenhal, 1810)   PLATE 21

Nationally Scarce B

Very local but often abundant when found in shallow water in ponds and seasonal fens, as at Shalford Meadows where it is abundant in shallow ditches and water under *Carex* beds. It is usually found in richly vegetated sites amongst submerged moss (including *Sphagnum*, although it is not a typical bog species) and other plants, but I have seen it swimming in large numbers over bare sand in North Hampshire at Woolmer Pond.

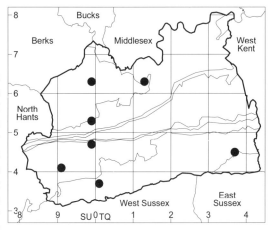

RECORDS – **Dunsfold**, 1976 (JAO), 2001-5 (JSD); **Black Pond, Esher**, 1976 (MS); **West End Common, Esher**, 5.1980 (JAO), 2002 (JSD); **Jacobs Well**, 1980 (JAO); **Chobham Common**, 1986 (RBA); **Shalford Meadows**, 1999, 5.2001, 5.2005 (JSD); **Blindley Heath**, 10.2001 (RDH); **Moat Pond, Thursley**, in *Sphagnum*, 2.6.2005 (JSD).

Hygrotus impressopunctatus

(Schaller, 1783)   PLATE 21

Local but occasionally abundant, primarily in ephemeral heathland pools but also in field ponds, as in Farnham Park, etc.

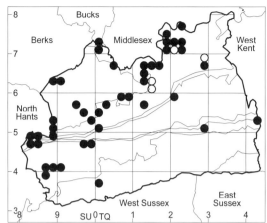

Hygrotus inaequalis

(Fabricius, 1777)   PLATE 21

Widespread and common in detritus ponds and at weedy margins of canals and lakes. Despite its near ubiquitous distribution, it has very rarely been taken in flight, although I once observed an adult at the tip of a *Typha* stem over 1.5m above the ground in the basin of a pond at Forest Green.

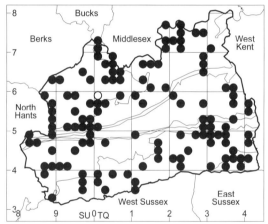

Hygrotus nigrolineatus

(Von Steven, 1835)   PLATE 21

Nationally Scarce A

Rare in sparsely vegetated or bare pools in sand pits. A recent arrival in Britain, first recorded in East Kent in 1983.

RECORDS – **Barnes WWT Centre**, 2000 (AH); **Richmond Park**, 5.2001 (DJL); **Beddington Sewage Farm**, 6.2002 (JSD).

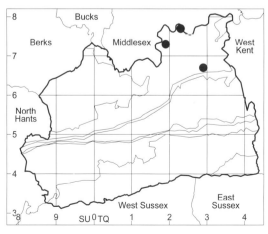

109

Hygrotus parallelogrammus (Ahrens, 1812)   PLATE 21

Nationally Scarce B

Primarily a halophile species of coastal pools and ditches, but it does occasionally breed in fresh-water sites, often in abundance.

RECORDS – **Wandsworth Common**, 1829 (A.Ingpen); **Richmond Park**, 1903 (THB); **Richmond Park: Ham Dip**, 24.9.1993 (MP).

Hygrotus versicolor

(Schaller, 1783)   PLATE 21

Rare. Associated with base-rich slow-flowing water in canals, also in large open ponds and lakes. It is locally abundant just a few kilometres into Berkshire, but I have not yet found it in Surrey.

RECORDS – **Wandsworth Common**, 1820 (A.Ingpen); **Woking**, 1890 (JAP); **Esher**, 1900 (THB); **Richmond Park**, 1900 (THB); **Basingstoke Canal, Mytchett**, 1942 (EAD); **Hedgecourt Lake**, 1956 (RR).

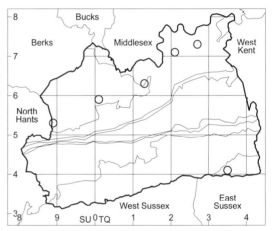

Hyphydrus ovatus

(Linnaeus, 1761)   PLATE 21

Widespread and often abundant in detritus ponds and small lakes, with adults found amongst submerged weed. I have never seen this beetle fly.

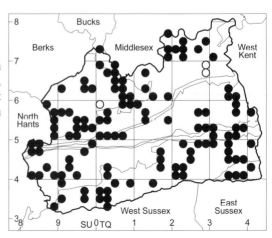

Laccornis oblongus (Stephens, 1835)   PLATE 21

Nationally Scarce A

Extinct. This is a very rare flightless species, found in ancient wetland sites. It is characteristic of pingos and other periglacial sites.

The only Surrey record is from **Chertsey** in 1901 (T.Hudson-Beare).

Laccophilus hyalinus

(Degeer, 1774)   PLATE 21

A greenish beetle, usually with pale flecking on the wing-cases. It is very local and largely restricted to slow-moving margins of rivers and canals. It also frequents the margins of wave-washed lakes, as at Coleford Lake, where speedboats create the waves. It is scarce in the dredged sections of the Basingstoke Canal, but abundant where weed persists. It is a strong flier, and singletons turn up in isolated ponds, as at Bookham Common, where it may well have been breeding.

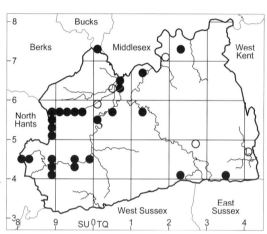

Laccophilus minutus

(Linnaeus, 1758)   PLATE 21

Widespread and often abundant in ponds and river edge habitats, but rare or absent from very acidic sites such as peat pools.

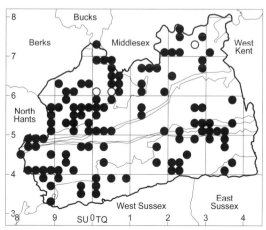

CARABIDAE – Ground Beetles

Many Carabids occur in wetlands and are regularly taken in the pond net, but one species, *Oodes helopioides*, actively hunts under water and is adapted to this amphibious mode of life to such an extent as to be worthy of inclusion as a water beetle. I was fortunate enough to take it in Surrey and observe and photograph its sub-aqua abilities. It is a strong swimmer, using a frenzied doggy-paddle, and also crawls rapidly up and down submerged plants and litter, and remains submerged for several minutes at a time. An air reservoir can be seen under the elytra.

Oodes helopioides (Fabricius, 1792)   PLATE 32

Swimming Ground Beetle

Nationally Scarce B

Rare, associated with weedy wetlands in pools and ditches.

RECORDS – **Wimbledon** in Fowler (1887); **Hoe Stream, Woking**, 1995 (AH); **Thundry Meadows** SWT reserve, trawled up in pond net from base of emergent *Typha* and *Scirpus*, 30.4.2005 (JSD).

Suborder POLYPHAGA

HYDROPHILOIDEA

HELOPHORIDAE

All but three of the twenty British Helophorids are aquatic, at least as adults. Most are to be found crawling around the margins of pools and ponds. They show a range of locomotive behaviour in water (Angus, 1966). Studying the intricate and often rapid movements of such diminutive creatures is far from easy, and only fully appreciable when slowed down. To this end the entomologist can either carry out his observations in the cold, where the reluctant subject may refuse to move at all, or alternatively employ some other cunning plan. Rob Angus's ingenious solution was to stick his subjects by their elytra to the head of a pin and submerge them in a 5% solution of methyl cellulose. Thus the bemused beetles had entered a slow-motion world, rather like forcing a human subject to swim through treacle! Some, like the common *H. minutus*, can actually dive and swim in open water, aided by fringes of hairs on the tarsi of the mid and hind legs. The hairs flare out at the start of the power stroke, remaining rigid as the leg sweeps back and providing more purchase against the water, like the blade of an oar. The return stroke is much faster as the hairs are 'feathered' and do not resist the water. The best, that the rest of the species which occur in Surrey can manage, is a sluggish dog-paddle to safety.

Helophorus aequalis

Thomson, C.G., 1868   PLATE 22

Widespread in seasonal pools, including wheel-rut pools, large puddles, and a wide variety of small ponds.

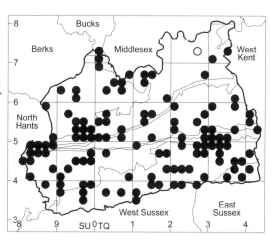

Helophorus alternans Gené, 1836

Nationally Scarce B

Rare, primarily coastal in pools and ditches, but recently discovered in mire habitat (similar to that used in the New Forest at its other inland sites).

RECORDS – **Merton** in Fowler (1889); **Pirbright Ranges: Strawberry Bottom**, in small *Sphagnum* pools, 8.2003 (JSD).

Helophorus arvernicus

Mulsant, 1846

Nationally Scarce B

In silt and mud at the edge of rivers. Locally abundant along the Wey.

RECORDS – **R.Wey: Woking**, 1980 (JAO); **Broadwater**, 6.2001; **Charterhouse**, 6.2001; **Eashing Valley**, 12.7.1994; **Thundry Meadows** SWT reserve, 5.1999; **Peper Harow**, 6.2000; **Somerset Bridge**, 5.2001; **Tilford**, 6.1998 (JSD).

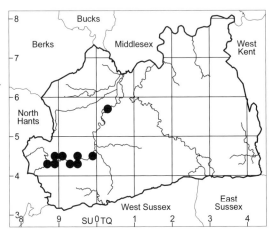

Helophorus brevipalpis

Bedel, 1881

Ubiquitous in stagnant waters, and regularly found raining down on cars and other shiny surfaces in hot weather. It occurs in the meanest waters, such as silt puddles and leaf-filled puddles, but avoids heavy shading.

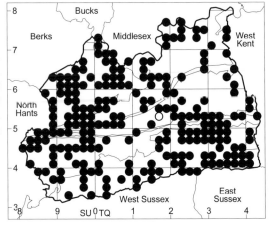

Helophorus dorsalis

(Marsham, 1802)   PLATE 22

Nationally Scarce B

In wheel-rut puddles filled with leaves in clayey woodland. The only modern record is from Bookham Common where it became very abundant in the Isle of Wight pond after it was excavated in 1992.

RECORDS – **Wimbledon Common**, 1829 (JFS); **Earlswood**, 1851 (JL); **Wandsworth Common** (JAP); **Ripley (Ockham Heath)** (JAP); **Claygate** (JAP); **Horsell Common**, 28.3.1900 (THB); **Bookham Common**, 5.1992 (JSD).

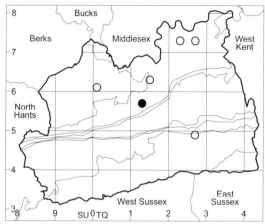

Helophorus flavipes

Fabricius, 1792

Widespread and locally abundant when found, in acid ponds, bog pools and shaded seepages.

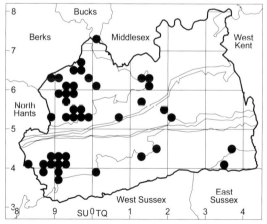

Helophorus grandis

Illiger, 1798   PLATE 22

Common in all kinds of stagnant waters, especially grassy field ponds and large puddles on silty substrates.

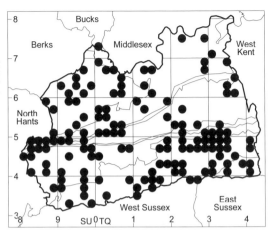

Helophorus granularis

(Linnaeus, 1760)

Nationally Scarce B

Very local, in ephemeral detritus ponds with grassy margins, especially in winter. Also in flushes in woodland amongst leaf litter.

RECORDS – **Box Hill**, 1890 (T.H.Hall); **Horsell**, 1909 (FB-B); **Bookham Common**, <1949 (AME lists); **Leith Hill**, 1978 (JAO); **Langham Pond**, 1986 (RBA); **Send Grove**, 3.9.2000; **Capel Clay Pit**, 9.2001; **Staffhurst Wood**, 2.2002 (JSD).

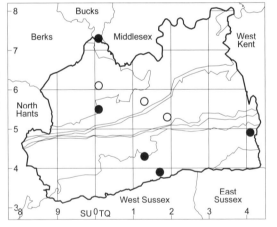

Helophorus griseus

Herbst, 1793

Nationally Scarce B

Very local and sporadic in silty areas at seasonal margins of pools.

RECORDS – **Langham Pond**, 1986 (RBA); **Brookwood**, 3.1996; **Farnham Park**, 5.1997, 5.1999; **Newdigate Brick Pits**, 3.2000; **Sidney Wood: Wey & Arun Canal**, 5.2000 (JSD).

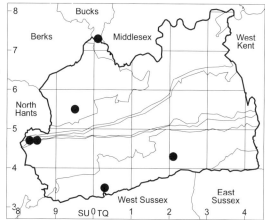

Helophorus laticollis Thomson, C.G., 1853

National Status: Vulnerable (RDB2)

Probably extinct in Surrey. In shallow detritus pools on heathland. Formerly found on Horsell Common and 'Woking', the last record being in 1929 (B.S.Williams). This species has been searched for at its old haunts by several Coleopterists without success, but it is a difficult species to find and easily overlooked, and so may await rediscovery.

RECORDS – **Horsell Common**, 1929 (BSW); **Woking**, 1905 (JJW).

Helophorus longitarsis

Wollaston, 1864

National Status: Rare (RDB3)

Rare in new silt pools, also at MV light.

RECORDS – **Beddington Sewage Farm**, at MV light, 17.8.1998 (D.A.Coleman, det. RGB) (Booth, 2000); **Ockley Green**, 6.2001 (JSD).

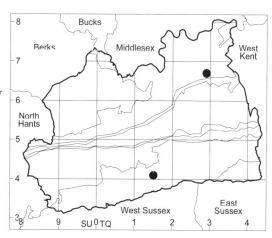

Helophorus minutus

Fabricius, 1775

Common in ephemeral ponds and puddles, especially in large puddles on clay and silt.

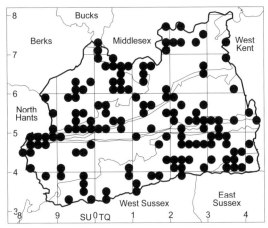

Helophorus nanus

Sturm, 1836

Nationally Scarce B

Rare in rich weedy ponds on heathland and in fens, and base-rich ponds.

RECORDS – **Bookham Common** <1940 (AME lists); **Black Pond, Esher**, 4.4.1976 (MS); **Jacobs Well**, 1970s (JAO); **Langham Pond, Runnymede**, 9.8.1986 (RGB).

Helophorus nubilus

Fabricius, 1777

A terrestrial species last recorded at Esher in the early 20th Century.

RECORDS – **Box Hill, Cobham & Mickleham** in Fowler (1888); **Claygate** & **Woking** (JAP).

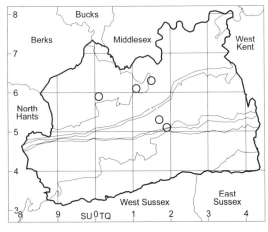

Helophorus obscurus

Mulsant, 1844

Common in a variety of ponds and at margins of flowing water, avoiding strongly acidic conditions.

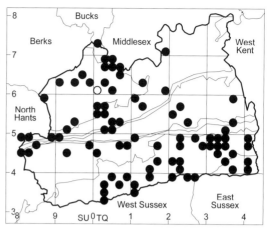

Helophorus porculus Bedel, 1881

Extinct. Last recorded at **Merton** in early 19th Century. A terrestrial species found on open ground on sand and clay. Can be abundant enough to cause serious damage to turnips, etc.

Helophorus rufipes (Bosc d'Antic, 1791)

Apparently a terrestrial species occurring at roots of plants, especially Brassicacae. No modern records, although still extant in North Hampshire.

RECORDS – **Merton** in Fowler (1888); **Esher**, 1907 (WES).

Helophorus strigifrons

Thomson, C.G., 1868

Nationally Scarce B

Rare in weedy temporary pools with rushes.

RECORDS – **Guildford**, 1909 (GCC); **Jacobs Well**, 1980 (JAO); **Chobham Common**, 1986 (RBA); **Blindley Heath**, 12.10.2001 (RDH).

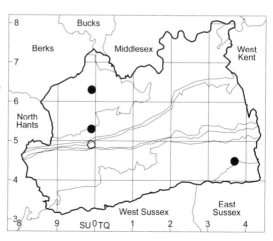

GEORISSIDAE – Mud-Coater Beetles

The only British Georissid is amongst the most tricky beetles to find, on account of its habit of coating itself with mud and grit. Adults live on moist open ground close to water. The best tactic is to splash water over likely-looking bare areas on the banks of the stream or river. The adults, fearing an imminent flood, miraculously emerge from the dirt and head up the slope.

The 'naked' beetles are black and of a very distinctive shape, but this is only visible after a good clean up!

Georissus crenulatus

(Rossi, 1794)   PLATE 22

Mud-coater Beetle

Nationally Scarce B

Rare. Occurs on exposed sediments beside rivers and pools. In Surrey it has been found on sandy margins of the River Wey, at **Wisley** in the early 20th Century by G.C.Champion, and at **Thundry Meadows** in 1999 (JSD).

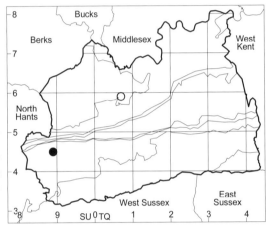

HYDROCHIDAE

Two of the seven British species occur in Surrey. They are elongate and distinctively sculptured beetles which move sluggishly through litter and debris at the margins of ponds and ditches.

Hydrochus angustatus

Germar, 1824   PLATE 22

Nationally Scarce B

Locally abundant in detritus ponds, and locally frequent on some heathlands, but not uncommon in richly vegetated field ponds on the Weald Clay.

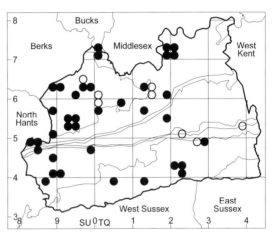

Hydrochus elongatus

(Schaller, 1783)   PLATE 22

National Status: Rare (RDB3)

Rare. I found it at Lakeside Park on 28.5.1999, in weedy margins of an old gravel pit pond.

RECORDS – **Bookham Common**, <1950 (AME lists); **Thundry Meadows** SWT reserve, 5.1994 (JSD); **Lakeside Park, Ash**, 5.1999 (JSD); **Runnymede**, 1986 (RBA), 2001 (NT).

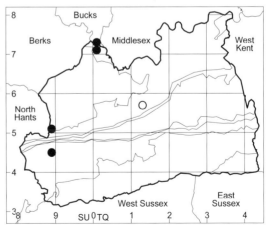

HYDROPHILIDAE – Water Scavenger Beetles

This diverse family includes free-swimming as well as semi-aquatic species, and terrestrial species primarily associated with dung and decaying organic matter. They range in size from 1mm to 48mm! The stronger-swimming species (*Berosus*, *Laccobius*) move by a rapid dog-paddling motion with limbs moved alternately. Most of the others do little more than crawl around under water. *Anacaena* species have the habit of walking on the underside of the surface film, where they are particularly conspicuous as the film of air on the underside of the body looks like mercury!

Most species can produce silk-like substances in order to protect their eggs, ranging from a few strands to secure eggs to plants, to large elaborate egg cocoons. *Helochares* carry the egg cocoons on the underside of the abdomen.

In all, 71 species are known from Britain, of which 21 are terrestrial and not included in this work.

Anacaena bipustulata

(Marsham, 1802)   PLATE 23

Nationally Scarce B

Widespread but local in muddy margins of rivers, canals and silty ponds. Absent from acidic areas.

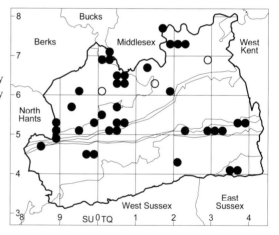

Anacaena globulus

(Paykull, 1798)   PLATE 23

All things considered, probably the most widespread water beetle in the county. Its larvae are terrrestrial and common in leaf litter. Adults are frequent around spring-heads, seepages, seasonally flooded ground and detritus ponds, especially in woods.

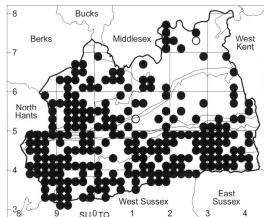

Anacaena limbata

(Fabricius, 1792)   PLATE 23

Widespread and frequent in stagnant water and at edges of springs and streams, usually in well-vegetated areas.

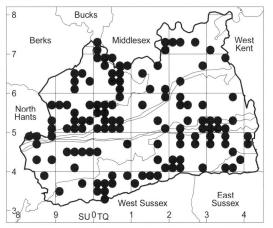

Anacaena lutescens

(Stephens, 1829)

Widespread and common around ponds and seepages, as well as weedy margins of rivers and canals.

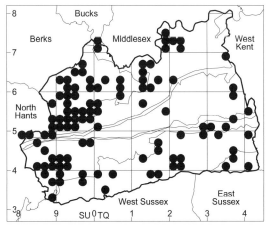

Paracymus scutellaris

(Rosenhauer, 1856)   PLATE 23

Nationally Scarce B

Rare in flowing water, including flushes, seepages and boggy streams on heathland. Recently rediscovered in small seepage pools in extensive mire areas on Pirbright ranges.

RECORDS – **Wimbledon Common**, 1868 (ECR); **Ashtead**, 1890 (HSD); **Horsell Common**, 1906 (ECB); **Bleak Inn**, 24.10.1909 (FB-B); **Pirbright Ranges: Strawberry Bottom & Colony Bog**, 24.7.2003 (JSD).

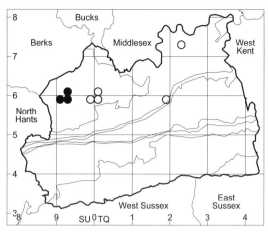

Genus *Berosus*

A small genus with four species found in Britain, three of which occur in Surrey. The fourth, *Berosus fulvus*, is a brackish-water species which has been taken at light at Greenwich, just inside West Kent. *Berosus* are distinctive free-swimming species. They can stridulate loudly, and specimens kept in aquaria are clearly audible over 3m away.

Berosus affinis

Brullé, 1835   PLATE 23

Nationally Scarce B

Local in silty ponds and sand-pit pools. A species which has become much more frequent over the past few decades. A strong swimmer, which can also stridulate.

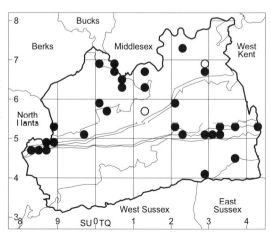

Berosus luridus

(Linnaeus, 1760)

Nationally Scarce B

Rare in ponds and ditches. It occurs on heathland but avoids the most acidic peat pools, occurring in more base-rich sites.

RECORDS – **Earlswood**, 1853-66 (JL); **Chobham Common**, 5.5.1900 (THB); **Horsell Common**, 1906 (ECB); **Woking**, 24.10.1909 (FB-B); **Bookham Common**, 1956 (D.G.Hall); **Black Pond, Esher**, 4.4.1976 (MS); **Ockham Common**, 1977 (PJH); **West End Common, Esher**, 1980 (JAO); **Jacobs Well**, 1980 (JAO).

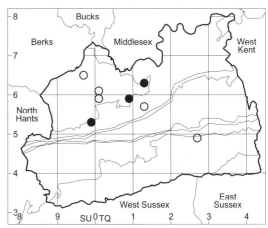

Berosus signaticollis

(Charpentier, 1825)   PLATE 23

Nationally Scarce B

Very local, but increasingly widespread. It is often abundant in weedy ponds, primarily on heathland, and in sand-pit pools.

RECORDS – **Earlswood**, 1850s (JL); **Mitcham**, 1898 (HH); **Chobham**, 1901 (THB); **Horsell Common**, 1906 (ECB); **Farnham Park**, 5.1998-9; **Churt Flashes**, 5.1998, 4.2000; **Moat Pond, Thursley**, 4.1998, 5.2000; **Thundry Meadows** SWT reserve, 5.1999 (JSD); **Bookham Common**, 30.9.2000 (MVLB); **Lakeside Park, Guildford**, 6.2001; **West End Common, Esher**, 5.2001; **Epsom Common**, 5.2002, **Chobham Common**, 4.2005 (JSD).

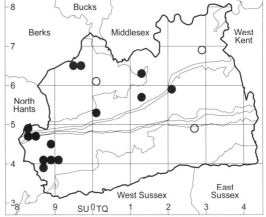

Chaetarthria seminulum (Herbst, 1797)

Nationally Scarce B

A tiny domed black beetle which is indistinguishable from *C. simillima* without dissection, and shares its habitats (Levey, 2005). Most previous records are referable to *C. simillima*, but the picture remains confused until male specimens can be found and dissected.

RECORD – **Clapham**, 20.8.1889 (SRA, det. BL).

Chaetarthria simillima

Vorst & Cuppen, 2003   PLATE 23

A tiny domed black beetle (1.0-1.5mm in length), which occurs in moss and muddy margins of standing and slow-flowing water.

RECORDS – **Esher**, 9.9.1908 (SRA); **Bookham Common**, 1913 (SRA, det. BL), 1937 (FJC); **Lakeside Park, Ash**, 5.1999; **Folly Bog**, 4-7.2000; **Gracious Pond**, 5.2000; **Pirbright Ranges: Strawberry Bottom**, 24.7.2003; **Century Range West**, 18.8.2003 (JSD).

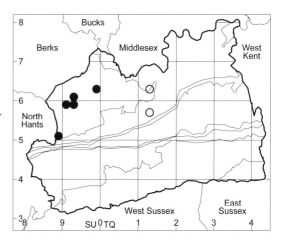

FURTHER RECORDS (for *C. seminulum sensu lato*) – **Wimbledon**, 1839 (JFS); **Barnes Common**, 1868 (ECR); **Woking**, 1927 (CET); **Jacobs Well**, 1980 (JAO).

Cymbiodyta marginellus

(Fabricius, 1792)   PLATE 24

A distinctive elongate all black species (reddish when teneral). It is local in detritus ponds, including heathland pools, but avoiding very acidic waters. It can thrive in very ephemeral pools, where numbers fluctuate markedly from year to year.

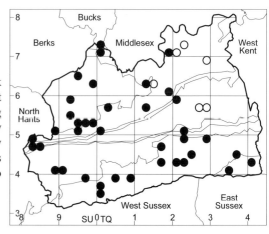

Enochrus affinis

(Thunberg, 1794)

Nationally Scarce B

Very local, but often abundant where found, in acidic heathland pools, preferring areas dominated by *Sphagnum*.

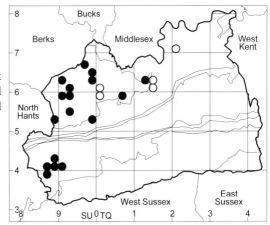

Enochrus bicolor (Fabricius, 1792)

Nationally Scarce B

Vagrant. A halophile species of coastal pools.

RECORD – **Wimbledon**, 1995, at light trap (det. JAO).

Enochrus coarctatus

(Gredler, 1863)   PLATE 24

Local in detritus pools and large bog pools with *Sphagnum*, and tolerant of partial shading. Characteristic of old long-established ponds, and present in the better village, Common and field ponds.

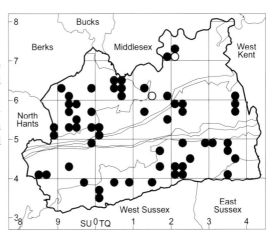

Enochrus melanocephalus

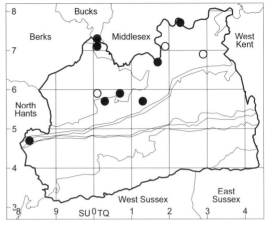

(Olivier, 1792)

Nationally Scarce B

Local but increasingly recorded inland. It frequents silt ponds, especially if newly created or cleared.

RECORDS – **Richmond Park**, 1899 (WES); **Mitcham**, 1899 (W.J.Fordham); **Woking**, 1907 (WES); **Runnymede**, 1988 (RBA), 2001 (NT); **Bookham Common**, 28.12.1996 (MVLB); **Surbiton, old water works**, in concrete-lined settling ponds, 4.1998 (JSD); **Bolder Mere**, 1999 (AH); **Farnham Park**, 5.1999 (JSD); **Barnes Wetland Centre**, 2000 (AH); **Papercourt marshes** SWT reserve, 8.2001 (JSD).

Enochrus nigritus Sharp, 1872 (= *isotae* Hebauer, 1981)

Nationally Scarce B

Rare in weedy fens and marshes.

RECORD – **Bookham Common**, before 1979 (GNF).

Enochrus ochropterus

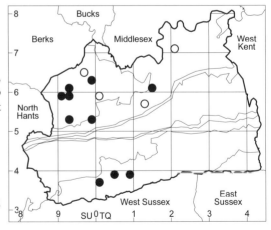

(Marsham, 1802)   PLATE 24

Nationally Scarce B

Rare in weedy pools on heathland, avoiding very acid conditions. Also in old richly vegetated ponds, as at Cranleigh and Ewhurst.

RECORDS – **Woking**, 1898 (AJC); **Richmond Park**, 1900 (THB); **Oxshott**, 1929 (JLH); **Bookham Common**, <1949 (Bookham List); **Dunsfold**, 1976; **Prince's Coverts**, 1978; **Jacobs Well**, 1980 (JAO): **Chobham Common**, 1986 (RBA); **Peatmoor Pond, Henley Park**, 4.1998; **Folly Bog**, 5.2000; **Cranleigh Village**, 3.2001; **Ewhurst Green**, 3.2001; **Pirbright Ranges: Strawberry Bottom**, 24.7.2003 (JSD).

Enochrus quadripunctatus (Herbst, 1797)

Nationally Scarce B

Rare, in *Sphagnum*-dominated pond at **Nower Wood** SWT reserve on 6.2001 (JSD).
This is a taxonomically problematic species which may be a form of *E. fuscipennis*.

Enochrus testaceus

(Fabricius, 1801)   PLATE 24

Local in detritus ponds, and usually found amongst submerged weed and litter at the margin of standing water.

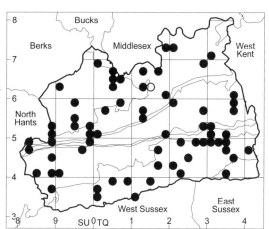

Helochares lividus

(Forster, 1771)

Widespread and locally abundant in litter and vegetation at margins of a wide range of ponds, especially on silty substrates. A rapid coloniser of new and recently cleared silt ponds. Scarce in acid waters, where largely replaced by *H. punctatus*, although both can occur together in mossy more base-rich sites such as shallow fen habitats.

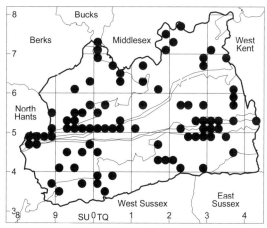

Helochares punctatus

Sharp, 1869   PLATE 23

Nationally Scarce B

Local but often extremely numerous in heathland ponds and bog pools. A strong flier and rapid coloniser of new heath pools. Increasingly recorded in flooded moss in richer shallow fen habitats, including shallow balancing ponds.

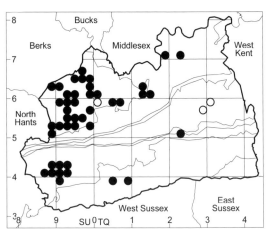

Hydrobius fuscipes

(Linnaeus, 1758)   PLATE 24

Common in still and slow-flowing water with abundant vegetation, including *Sphagnum* pools. It is a variable species with forms which various authors have attempted to raise to subspecies level.

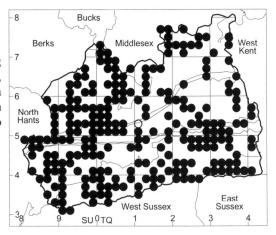

Hydrochara caraboides (Linnaeus, 1758)   PLATE 25
Lesser Silver Water Beetle

National Status: Endangered (RDB1) (but **RDB3** would be more appropriate)

Extinct. Associated with marsh dykes and old richly vegetated field ponds with abundant aquatic molluscs upon which the larvae feed. Comes to light.

RECORD – **Wimbledon**, 5.1874 (EAW).

Hydrophilus piceus (Linnaeus, 1758)   PLATE 25
Great Silver Water Beetle
National Status: Rare (RDB3)

Extinct. Associated with marsh dykes and occasionally in richly vegetated ponds with abundant aquatic molluscs upon which the larvae feed. It is a strong flier and comes readily to light.

RECORDS – Balfour-Browne (1958) gives Surrey as a county for this species, but he lists **Camberwell** amongst a list of West Kent sites including Lewisham, Lee and Plumstead, all of which are very close to the county boundary. John Clegg introduced adults to a pond at **Haslemere Museum** in the early 1960s.

Genus *Laccobius*

With the exception of two probable vagrant species, all seven of the established British *Laccobius* occur in Surrey. They are rather similar-looking insects which can be tricky to identify, and in some species only the males can be named with certainty. They are domed insects (2.5-4.0mm in length) and all have a dark central mark on the pronotum, which often has a metallic greenish tinge. The strongly punctured elytra vary from very pale (*minutus, sinuatus*) to almost black (*atratus*).

Laccobius atratus

Rottenberg, 1874

Nationally Scarce B

Rare in acid seepages, bogs and mires. It is associated with areas with some flow, and rarely occurs in stagnant peat pools.

RECORDS – **Chobham**, 1900 (GCC); **Rowhill LNR**, 5.1998; **Folly Bog**, 5.2000 (JSD); **Wisley Common**, 2001 (AS); **Pirbright Ranges: Strawberry Bottom**, 24.7.2003 (JSD).

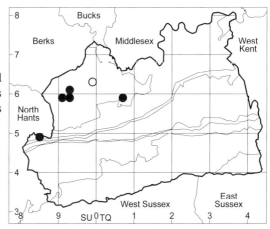

131

Laccobius bipunctatus

(Fabricius, 1775)   PLATE 23

Widespread and abundant, especially in mud at the edges of ponds, canals and running water in open situations.

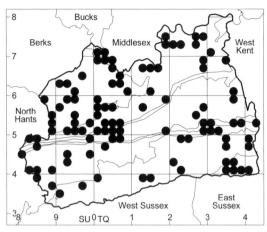

Laccobius colon

(Stephens, 1829)

(= *biguttatus* Gerhardt, 1877)

Rare in weedy ponds.

RECORDS – **Woking**, 19th Century (JAP); **Frensham**, 1900 (JJW); **Richmond**, 1900 (THB); **Bookham Common**, 1939, 1940 (FJC); **Prince's Coverts**, 1978 (JAO); **Tandridge Hill**, 3.5.1986 (JHB); **Runnymede**, 2001 (NT); **Woking: Westfield**, 3.2002 (JSD).

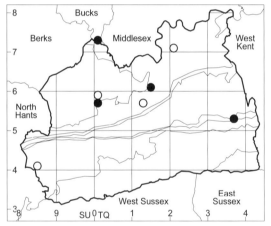

Laccobius minutus

(Linnaeus, 1758)

Ponds and riversides with soft substrates.

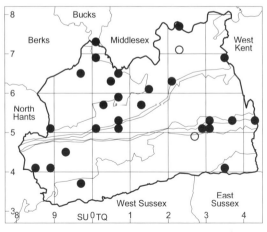

Laccobius sinuatus

Motschulsky, 1849

Nationally Scarce B

Silty margins of rivers, and sandpits.

RECORDS – **Bookham Common**, 1914 (SRA), 1935 (FJC); **The Moors, Redhill**, 6.2001; **Beddington Sewage Farm**, 2002; **Guildford Research Park**, 8.2003; **Thorpe**, 4.2003 (JSD).

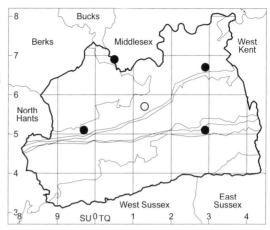

Laccobius striatulus

(Fabricius, 1801)

Silt at edge of streams and rivers. Seems to prefer substrates without *obvious* organic enrichment.

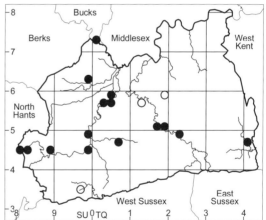

Laccobius ytenensis

Sharp, 1910

(= *atrocephalus* Reitter, 1872)

Nationally Scarce B

Rare in seepages on heathland in the Thames basin. Like *L. atratus* it is associated with areas with some flow, and rarely occurs in stagnant peat pools.

RECORDS – **Wimbledon Common**, 1945 (KGB); **Rowhill LNR**, in the small bog which straddles the Hampshire-Surrey border at the head of the Blackwater, 3.1998; **Folly Bog**, 2000; **Hambledon Clay Pits**, 9.2000 (JSD).

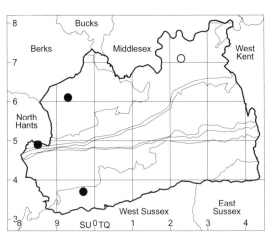

Sphaeridiinae

This subfamily includes several semi-aquatic and terrestrial species. In addition to the primarily aquatic species described below, there are a further 12 *Cercyon* species known from Surrey which occur in dung and other decaying vegetable matter, along with the four species of *Sphaeridium* and three species of *Cryptopleurum*. For further information on these species, see Denton (2004).

Coelostoma orbiculare

(Fabricius, 1775)   PLATE 24

Locally abundant in damp, detritus-rich sites including bogs, ponds and canal margins. It can occur at the base of emergent vegetation such as sedges growing in *Sphagnum*. It can often be found out of water in damp litter and moss, but invariably close to water.

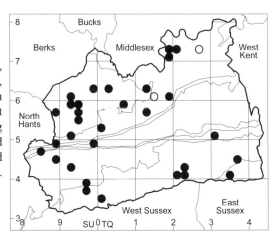

Cercyon bifenestratus

Küster, 1851

Nationally Scarce A

Rare on exposed sediments such as silt and sand at margins of rivers and ponds.

RECORDS – **Thundry Meadows** SWT reserve, on banks of R.Wey where the sand had been enriched with the droppings of Canada Geese, 5.1999; **Somerset Bridge**, 5.2001 (JSD).

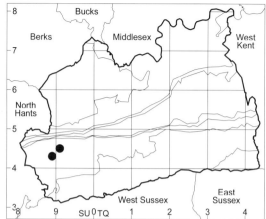

Cercyon convexiusculus

Stephens, 1829

Local but often abundant in detritus and rotting leaf litter, and in moss around richly vegetated sites.

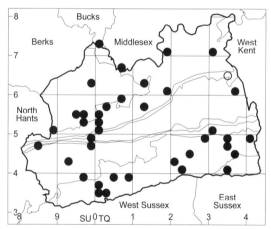

Cercyon granarius Erichson, 1837

National Status: Rare (RDB3)

Rare, and largely restricted to the Thames Valley where it resides in wetlands on the flood-plain. Most records are from flood refuse and tussocks in winter, and its summer habits are very poorly known.

RECORD – **Runnymede: Langham Pond**, 8.2.1990 (RBA).

Cercyon marinus

Thomson, C.G., 1853   PLATE 24

Local in waterside detritus, but also in damp litter away from water, such as piles of water-weed removed from ponds.

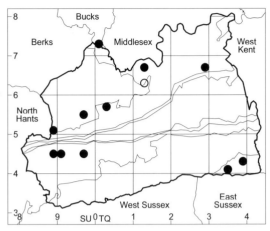

Cercyon sternalis

Sharp, 1918

Nationally Scarce B

Rare and local in reed and sedge litter.

RECORDS – **Runnymede: Langham Pond**, 1986, 1988 (RBA); **Bookham Common**, 28.7.1998 (RGB); **Esher Common**, 1999; **Blindley Heath**, 5.1999; **Hedgecourt Lake**, 6.2001; **Rickford Common**, 6.2001; **Pirbright**, 6.2001; **Papercourt** SWT reserve, 6.2001; **Epsom Common**, 22.5.2001; **Whitebushes**, 8.2002 (JSD).

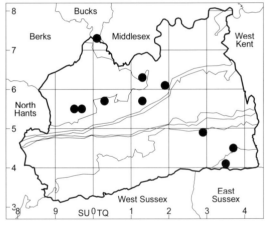

Cercyon tristis

(Illiger, 1801)

Nationally Scarce B

Very rare in reed and fen litter around older ponds and pools.

RECORDS – **Arbrook Common**, 21.5.1944 (JB-B), **Bay Pond** SWT reserve, 5.2000 (JSD).

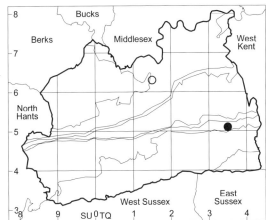

Cercyon ustulatus

(Preyssler, 1790)

Nationally Scarce B

Mossy areas of ponds and also on muddy riverbanks. I recently found it in moss on top of sewage filter beds at Guildford Water Works.

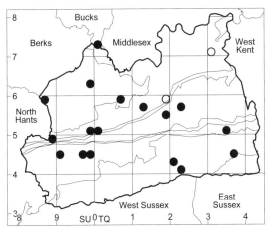

Megasternum concinnum (Marsham, 1802)

(= *obscurum* (Marsham, 1802))

Common in wet detritus at edge of water, but also abundant in terrestrial habitats such as compost heaps. Frequently taken in flight.

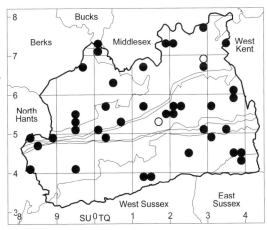

HYDRAENIDAE

Thirty species of Hydraenids are known to occur in Britain, all of which are less than 4mm in length, and some are less than 2mm long! *Ochthebius* are all heavily sculptured insects, the differences in sculpture being a considerable aid to their identification. Habitat selection is diverse for such a small family, with some stream specialists. Adults do not swim freely but crawl amongst weed in a wide variety of aquatic habitats, from streams and ponds to brackish pools, while the larvae are terrestrial or semi-aquatic.

Hydraena britteni

Joy, 1907

Rare. On the Trust reserve at Thundry Meadows it occurs in small partially-shaded boggy pools at the edge of Joyce's Meadow. It often lives amongst grass at margins of slow-flowing water.

RECORDS – **Dorking**, 1976 (JAO); **Thundry Meadows**, 1999 (JSD).

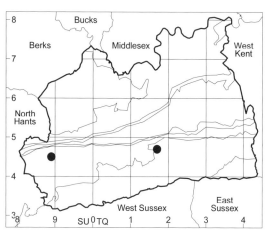

Hydraena gracilis

Germar, 1824

Very local in running water. Adults occur amongst submerged gravel in swift-flowing sections. Also on stones and around submerged tree roots.

RECORDS – **Hazelbridge**, 4.1995; **Imbhams Farm stream**, 9.2000; **Devil's Punchbowl to Dye House, Thursley**, 9.2000; **Pignuts Copse**, 9.2000 (JSD).

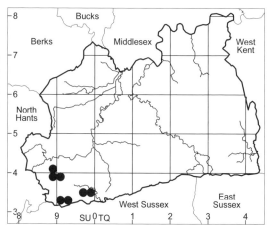

Hydraena nigrita

Germar, 1824

Nationally Scarce B

A running water species, found in small feeder streams on clay. Adults are usually found on a mineral substrate, amongst stones or under lumps of clay, and also amongst submerged tree roots. It avoids organic substrates such as peat.

SELECTED RECORDS –
Dunsfold, 1976 (JAO);
Hazelbridge, 18.4.1995; **Wallis Wood** SWT reserve, 6.1999;
Park Copse, 9.2000; **Vann Lake** SWT reserve, 4.2001; **Paynes Green**, 2001; **Birches Wood**, 2001; **Lyne House Woods**, 3.2001; **The Jordans** (2038), 3.2001; **Holmwood Corner**, 2001; **Frillinghurst Wood**, 3.2005; **Hambledon House**, 8.2006 (JSD).

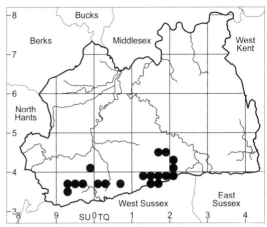

Hydraena riparia

Kugelann, 1794   PLATE 21

Widespread and locally abundant beside still and running water. It occurs in weedy pond margins but is equally at home in litter and silt at margins of barren woodland streams devoid of plant life.

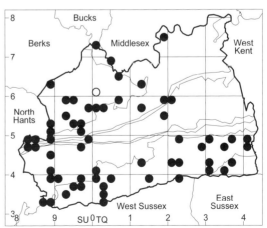

Hydraena rufipes

Curtis, 1830

Nationally Scarce B

Very local and restricted to small feeder streams on clay.

RECORDS – **Blackbrook, near Stonebridge**, 1989 (TDH); **Hazelbridge**, 1995; **Holmwood Corner**, 2001; **Stream south of Holmwood** (TQ1844), 3.2001 (JSD).

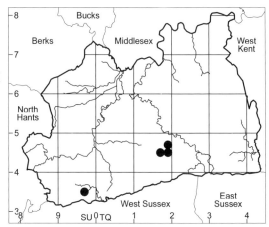

Hydraena testacea

Curtis, 1830

Nationally Scarce B

Local but usually abundant where found. It normally lives amongst rotting leaves at the margins of still or slow-moving water. Also found on stones at edge of rivers. Tolerant of shading.

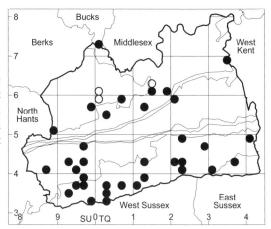

Limnebius aluta Bedel, 1881

National status: Rare (RDB3)

Probably extinct, although it could be overlooked through being one of the smallest water beetles at a little over 1mm in length. It lives in fens at margins of pools and ditches. Only record is from **Wimbledon Common** in 1829 (EAW).

Limnebius nitidus

(Marsham, 1802)

Nationally Scarce B

At muddy margins of ponds and flowing water.

RECORDS – **Wimbledon**, 1829 (M.Waterhouse); **Earlswood**, 1856 (JL); **Richmond Park**, 1900 (THB); **Black Pond, Esher**, 1900 (THB); **Epsom Common**, 1976 (JAO); **Runnymede**, 1988 (RBA); **Bookham Common**, 11.10.1995 (PJH).

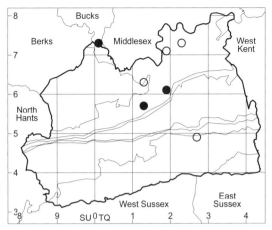

Limnebius papposus

Mulsant, 1844

Nationally Scarce B

Rare, in weedy ponds. The only modern record is from Felcourt Wood in 1990 (ITE survey, det. GNF).

RECORDS – **Barnes Common**, 1827 (ECR); **Earlswood**, 1856 (JL); **Mitcham**, 1900 (HH); **Felcourt Wood**, 1990 (ITE).

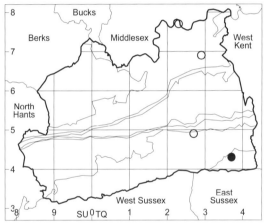

Limnebius truncatellus

(Thunberg, 1794)   PLATE 21

Widespread and common at edges of ponds and beside flowing water. Frequent in springs and seepages in woods.

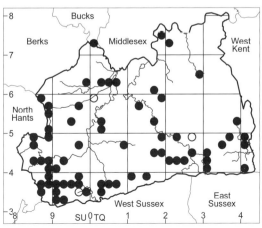

141

Ochthebius aeneus Stephens, 1835

National status: Endangered (RDB1)

Extinct. Formerly found in small heathland pools at **Horsell**, **Woking**, **Putney** and **Wandsworth** in 19th Century. Last recorded in Britain in 1913 in Sussex.

Ochthebius bicolon

Germar, 1824

Nationally Scarce B

Widespread but local at margins of streams, often in shade, in root tangles, and debris. Also in shallow muddy ditches.

RECORDS – **Bookham Common**, 1946 (AME); **Blackbrook, near Stonebridge**, 1989 (TDH); **Hazelbridge**, 5.1992-2002 (JSD); **Wallis Wood** SWT reserve, 7.1999 (JSD); **Vann Lake** SWT Reserve, 5.2001 (JSD).

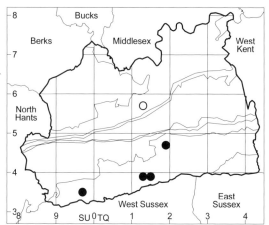

Ochthebius dilatatus

Stephens, 1829

Very scarce in pools and seepages especially on clayey substrates.

RECORDS – **Claygate**, 1860 (JAP); **Chertsey Meads**, 1999 (DAL); **Newdigate Brick Pits**, 2000; **Hambledon Clay Pits**, 9.2000; **Capel Clay Pit**, 9.2001; **Beddington Sewage Farm**, 7.2002 (JSD).

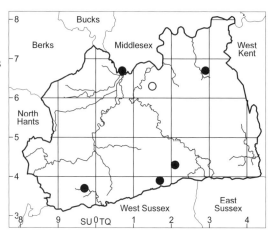

Ochthebius minimus

(Fabricius, 1792)   PLATE 21

Common at margins of ponds and flowing water, but avoids bog and peat pools.

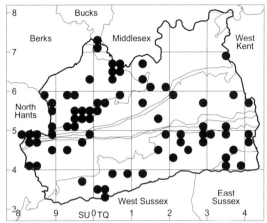

Ochthebius pusillus

Stephens, 1835

National status: Rare (RDB3)

Rare. Found in mud and silt around the margins of ponds. A pioneer species which colonises new and recently cleared ponds. Abundant on Bookham Common.

RECORDS – **Bookham Common**, 11.10.1995 (PJH); **Newdigate Brick Pits**, 10.2000; **Capel Clay Pit**, 9.2.2001 (JSD).

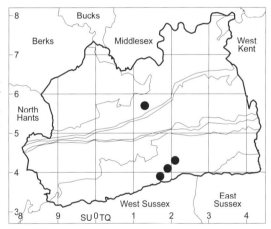

Ochthebius viridis Peyron, 1858

Nationally Scarce B

Probably vagrant. This is usually a coastal insect associated with brackish pools, and ditches on grazing levels.

RECORD – **Ranmore Common**, 4.8.1923 (JLH).

SCIRTOIDEA

SCIRTIDAE – Marsh Beetles

Semi-aquatic beetles, with larvae which develop in fresh water, including the smallest water bodies used by any British water beetle (see *Prionocyphon*). The adults are all terrestrial, somewhat delicate, free-flying insects, usually encountered on foliage and in some instances on blossoms. Twenty species occur in Britain.

Elodes elongata

Tournier, 1868

(= *koelleri* Klausnitzer, 1971)

PLATE 26

Local by streams and wetlands, preferring richer waters such as chalk streams. Adult from May to August.

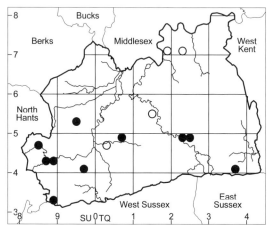

Elodes minuta

(Linnaeus, 1758)   PLATE 26

Local, with adults on trees and bushes by base-poor streams. Adult from May to August.

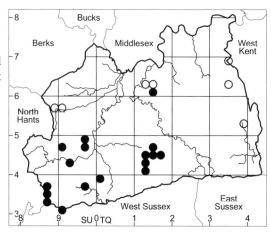

Elodes tricuspis Nyholm, 1985

National Status: Rare (RDB3)

A rare species with only five known sites in Britain, most of which are old parkland sites, but in at least one of them it was associated with a fairly ordinary-looking stream.

The only Surrey specimen was one male taken by A.E.Gardner at **Frensham** on 26.6.1954 (det. JSD).

Odeles (=Elodes) marginata

(Fabricius, 1798)   PLATE 26

Very local. Larvae in shaded streams and spring-heads, and adults nearby on foliage. In northern England this is primarily a species of open streams on moorland, so perhaps its association with shaded woodland streams in the south is related to a need for cooler and more humid conditions.

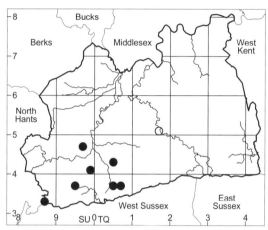

RECORDS – **Dorking**, 1900 (AJC, det. JSD); **Cucknells Wood** SWT reserve, 5.2000; **Hammer Bottom**, 5.2000; **Bummoor Copse**, 6.2003; **Cobblers Brook**, 5.2005; **Vachery Pond**, 6.2005; **Winkworth Arboretum**, 5.2005; **Hartsgrove Hanger**, 6.2006 (JSD).

Microcara testacea

(Linnaeus, 1767)   PLATES 26, 27

Adults on blossoms in the spring and occur throughout the summer. Larvae are often abundant in winter and spring in leaf-filled pools, especially in woodland.

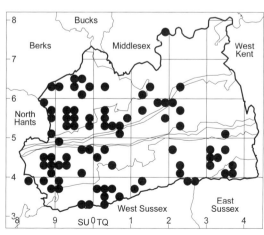

Cyphon coarctatus

Paykull, 1799

Widespread and locally abundant, with larvae especially abundant in partly shaded sites with rotting leaf litter.

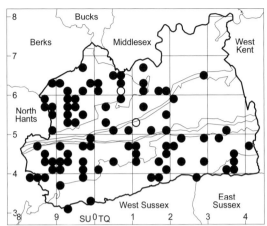

Cyphon hilaris

Nyholm, 1944

Local in wetlands with peaty substrates and frequent on wet heathland sites, but may also be found in fen areas as at **Hedgecourt Lake** and **Bay Pond** SWT reserves.

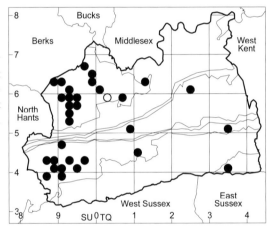

Cyphon laevipennis

Tournier, 1868

(= *phragmiteticola* Nyholm, 1955)

Rare in Surrey, on tall emergent vegetation at margins of lakes and ponds.

RECORDS – **West Byfleet**, 1932 (FJC); **Blindley Heath**, 1999 (JSD); **Farnham: Bourne Mill**, 6.2002; **Brooklands Airfield**, 5.2004; **Papercourt marshes** SWT reserve, 4.2004 (JSD).

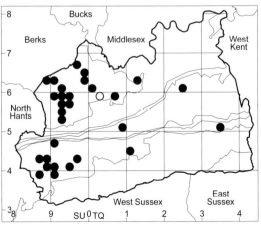

Cyphon ochraceus

Stephens, 1830

Local in marshes, fens and richer wetlands. Absent from acid mire areas.

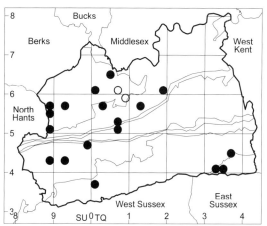

Cyphon padi

(Linnaeus, 1758)   PLATE 26

Widespread, especially in wooded habitats, with a preference for peaty areas with flooded *Sphagnum*. Adults overwinter and are active on blossom in early spring.

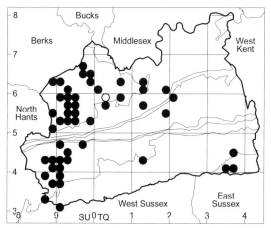

Cyphon palustris Thomson, 1855

Rare, near streams. The larvae develop in submerged gravel.

RECORDS – **Virginia Water** (PJH); **Bagmoor Common**, 5.1998 (RDH); **Royal Common**, 6.2001 (JSD).

Cyphon pubescens

(Fabricius, 1792)

Nationally Scarce B

Rare, with adults on foliage and also on blossom of blackthorn in spring. Associated with richer heathland ponds.

RECORDS – **Peatmoor Pond, Henley Park**, 4.1998; **Blindley Heath**, 5.1999 (JSD), 9.2001, 5.2002 (RDH); **Bolder Mere**, 6.1999 (JSD); **Wisley RHS Gardens**, 9.2006 (RDH).

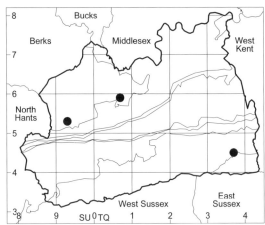

Cyphon variabilis

(Thunberg, 1787)   PLATE 26

Locally abundant in a wide variety of standing waters from weedy pond and lake margins to smaller peat pools in carr and damp heathland. Overwinters as an adult, when it can be found in reedmace stems. Active on blossom, especially cherry-plum and blackthorn in March and April.

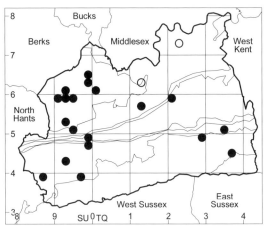

Prionocyphon serricornis

(Müller, P.W.J., 1821)   PLATES 26, 27

The Tree-hole Beetle

Nationally Scarce B

Breeds exclusively in phytothelms (rot-holes and root-plate pools) in trees. Widespread and common in areas with beech trees, but easily overlooked in other wooded areas. Overwinters as a larva which is nearly full-grown by spring. Adults are very rarely encountered.

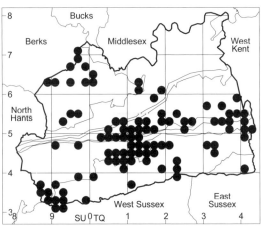

Scirtes hemisphaericus

(Linnaeus, 1758)   PLATE 27

Local on marginal vegetation of ponds and ditches, avoiding very acidic sites.

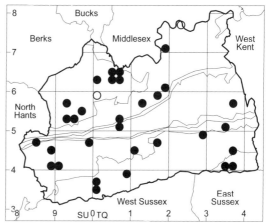

Scirtes orbicularis (Panzer, 1793)   PLATE 26

Nationally Scarce A

Extinct. Restricted to grazing marshes and fens.

RECORDS – **Merton** and **Esher** in Fowler (1890).

ELMIDAE – Riffle Beetles

Small beetles including several restricted to swift-flowing water, where the adults live completely submerged and breathe with the aid of a plastron (a thin film of air held around the body surface which acts like a physical gill), extracting all their gaseous needs from the water. Twelve species occur in Britain.

Elmis aenea

(Müller, P.W.J., 1806)   PLATE 25

Common in flowing water habitats, clinging to submerged stones, logs and tree roots. Also not infrequently taken in flight.

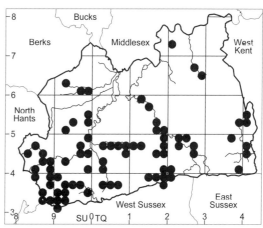

Limnius volckmari

(Panzer, 1793)   PLATE 25

Local in flowing water habitats, especially with coarse substrates, in open and shaded situations.

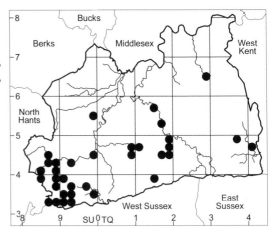

Riolus cupreus (Müller, P.W.J., 1806)

Nationally Scarce B

Probably extinct. Associated with base-rich running water, unpolluted streams and rivers.
RECORD – **Ripley**, **Woking** (GCC).

Riolus subviolaceus (Müller, P.W.J., 1817)

Nationally Scarce B

Rare but probably under-recorded in streams. The only record to date comes from a small weir in the **Gibbs Brook**, a very ordinary-looking stream crossing clayey arable land, 8.2000 (JSD).

Oulimnius tuberculatus

(Müller, P.W.J., 1806)   PLATE 25

Local in flowing water, especially in root tangles. Also in the Basingstoke Canal under overhanging tussocks, 1999 (JSD).

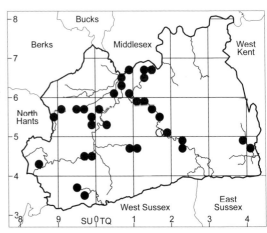

Oulimnius rivularis (Rosenhauer, 1856)
Nationally Scarce B
Probably extinct. Associated with margins of large drains, **Woking**, 1870 (JAP).

Oulimnius troglodytes (Gyllenhal, 1827)
Nationally Scarce B
Listed in VCH. Probably extinct. Found in flowing water, and wave-washed lakes.

DRYOPIDAE – Hairy Crawling Water Beetles
Distinctive hirsute beetles, which can live underwater. The thick pile of hair over the body maintains a complete coat of air. The larvae are elongate and terrestrial. Adult *Dryops ernesti* can also be found in dry sandy places away from water.

Pomatinus substriatus (Müller, P.W.J., 1806)   PLATE 27
Nationally Scarce A
Rare, possibly extinct. It lives on submerged logs in swift-flowing streams and rivers, and is therefore easily overlooked.
RECORD – **Chiddingfold**, c.1900 (HSD), presumably in the Hazelbridge stream which looks suitable for this species.

Dryops auriculatus (Fourcroy, 1785)
Nationally Scarce B
Rare, possibly extinct. Associated with fens, and other base-rich wetlands.
RECORDS – **Mitcham Common**, <1927 (JLH); **Bookham Common**, 1932 (FJC).

Dryops ernesti

des Gozis, 1886

Rare in sandy open areas, including river edges and heath ponds. Adults can be found in dry areas in summer, but these are invariably subject to inundation in winter floods.

RECORDS – **Mitcham Common**, <1927 (JLH); **Pyrford**, 1994 (RGB); **Thundry Meadows**, 5.1999 (JSD).

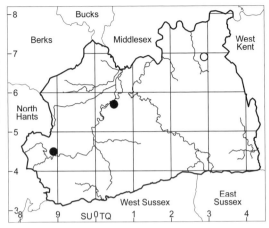

Dryops luridus

(Erichson, 1847)   PLATE 27

Much the commonest Dryopid in Surrey. It is locally abundant at the margins of ponds and streams in both muddy and vegetated areas.

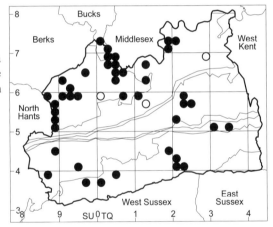

Dryops similaris Bollow, 1936

National Status: Rare (RDB3)

Associated with fen pools.

Only record is from **Morden** in 1865 (DS).

Dryops striatellus

(Fairmaire & Brisout, 1859) PLATE 27

National Status: Rare (RDB3)

Confined to shallow ephemeral heathland pools. It has benefited from the creation of breeding sites for Natterjack Toads on Churt Flashes, and in North Hampshire.

RECORDS – **Wimbledon**, 1866 (DS); **Horsell**, 1898 (THB), 1906 (ECB); **Woking**, 1914 (JJW); **Churt Flashes**, 1994-98, **Brentmoor Heath**, 4.2007 (JSD).

HETEROCERIDAE – Burrowing Mud Beetles

Attractively marked semi-aquatic beetles, found at the margins of water in burrows in damp silt, sand or mud. They are strong fliers, and readily take to the air when disturbed. The larvae are terrestrial.

Heterocerus fenestratus

(Thunberg, 1784)   PLATE 27

Widespread in exposed sediments (mud, sand and silt) at margins of ponds, lakes and rivers. It is a strong flier, often taken at light traps.

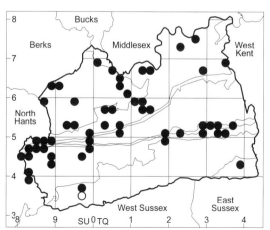

Heterocerus fossor Kiesenwetter, 1843

Perhaps vagrant, or extinct in Surrey. A coastal species found in mud and silt in saltmarshes, etc. As with its relatives, it is a strong flier and could turn up anywhere.

RECORD – Reputedly taken at **Claygate** (Clarke, 1973).

Heterocerus marginatus

(Fabricius, 1787)

Local in exposed sediments, especially sand and silt on the banks of the River Wey, often in the company of *H. fenestratus*, from which it can be separated by the absence of orange marks extending onto the front edge of the elytra.

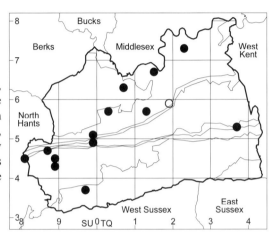

CHRYSOMELIDAE – Leaf Beetles

Donaciinae – Reed Beetles

Donaciinae is a small subfamily of semi-aquatic leaf beetles. The larvae develop at the roots of water plants. Adults are attractive free-flying species, which feed on the leaves and pollen of water plants, often on the same species utilised by the larvae.

Donacia aquatica (Linnaeus, 1758)
Zircon Reed Beetle

National Status: Rare (RDB3)

Extinct in Surrey. [On sedges (*Carex*) in wetlands.]

RECORDS – **Battersea** in Fowler (1890); Last recorded at **Chiddingfold** in 1912 by Horace Donisthorpe.

Donacia bicolora

Zschach, 1788   PLATE 28

Golden Reed Beetle

National Status: Vulnerable (RDB2)

Local on branched bur-reed growing at margins of rivers and standing water, including ponds and lakes. It is locally abundant on open sections of the River Wey downstream from Godalming. It was abundant along the Basingstoke Canal before boat traffic and dredging resumed. Surrey is a national stronghold for this species.

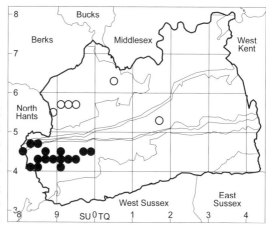

Donacia cinerea

Herbst, 1784   PLATE 28

Hairy Reed Beetle

Nationally Scarce B

Local on reedmace and lesser reedmace.

RECORDS – **Byfleet**, 1927 (FJC); **Mytchett Lake**, 1940 (EAD); **Bolder Mere**, 1990 (ISM), 2000 (JSD); **Black Pond, Esher**, 6.1995; **Virginia Water**, 5.1996; **Thursley Hammer Pond**, 5.1996; **Newdigate Brick Pits**, 6.2000, 27.5.2005; **Wey Meadows**, 6. 2001; **Mill Pond, Weybridge**, 6.2001 (JSD); **Hedgecourt Lake**, 6.2004 (RDH).

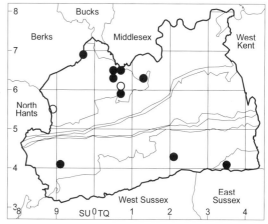

Donacia clavipes

Fabricius, 1792   PLATE 28

Yellow-legged Reed Beetle

Nationally Scarce B

Local on reeds. Adults shelter in the leaf rolls, often in numbers. They chew through the developing rolled-up leaves which, once they unfurl, leave a neat line of holes.

RECORDS – **Byfleet**, 1927; **Albury Pond**, 1934 (FJS); **Frensham Great Pond**, 5.1996; **Coleford Lake**, 6.1999; **Black Pond, Esher**, 6.2000; **Thundry Meadows** SWT reserve 6.2000; **Hatchlands, Sheepwash Pond**, 6.2001; **R.Wey, Broadmead**, 6.2001; **Lakeside Park, Guildford**, 6.2002; **Clandon Park**, 6.2006 (JSD).

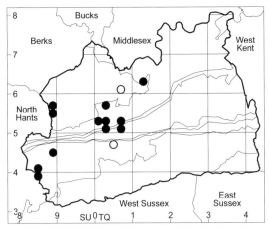

Donacia crassipes Fabricius, 1775   PLATE 28

Water-lily Reed Beetle

Nationally Scarce B

Rare, possibly extinct. On white and yellow water-lilies.

Still extant a few kilometres into North Hampshire at Yateley Common.

RECORD – **Weybridge** in Fowler (1890).

Donacia dentata Hoppe, 1795

Arrowhead Reed Beetle

Nationally Scarce A

Extinct in Surrey, but formerly on arrowhead at **Chobham** (Fowler, 1890).

Donacia impressa Paykull, 1799   PLATE 28

Nationally Scarce A

Rare on bulrush (*Scirpus*) and sedges, including tussock sedge and lesser pond sedge.

RECORDS – **Newdigate Brick Pits**, on grey bulrush, 5.2000, 27.5.2005 (JSD).

Donacia marginata

Hoppe, 1795   PLATE 28

Local on bur-reed (*Sparganium*). Most records come from plants of branched bur-reed growing in still or slow-flowing water.

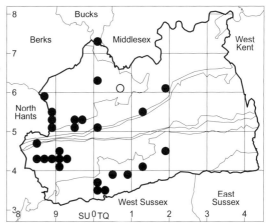

Donacia obscura Gyllenhal, 1813
Chocolate Reed Beetle
Nationally Scarce A

Rare, on bottle sedge. Only known from **Thursley Common** NNR where it was taken in May 1992 (JSD) and again in February 1998 (R.M.Fry), an extraordinary record. This is the only modern locality in southern Britain, so this is yet another primarily northern species for which Thursley appears to be (or, alas, in some cases once was) the last outpost, joining the likes of White-faced Darter dragonfly, *Leucorrhinia dubia*, the water bug *Glaenocorisa propinqua* and the hoverfly *Anasimyia lunulata*.

Donacia semicuprea

Panzer, 1796
Sweet-Grass Reed Beetle

Local on reed sweet-grass, mainly beside still water. The adults graze the surface of the *Glyceria* leaves causing extensive necrosis. In late summer the browning leaves become very distinctive, mapping out the beetle's activities!

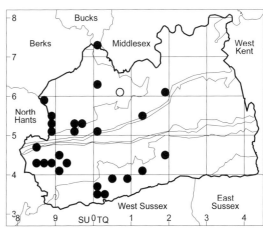

Donacia simplex

Fabricius, 1775   PLATE 28

Widespread and often locally abundant on bur-reed, mostly branched bur-reed growing beside rivers, lakes, ponds and canals. As with *D. semicuprea*, the host plant goes prematurely brown where it has been grazed by this species and, at some sites, *D. bicolora* and *D. marginata*.

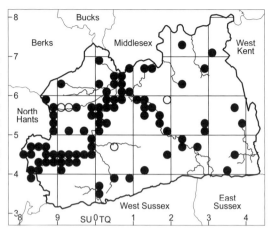

Donacia sparganii Ahrens, 1810

Nationally Scarce A

Rare nationally and possibly extinct in Surrey. On bur-reed. Formerly taken near **Wandsworth** on banks of the River Thames and at **Weybridge** (HSD). In some rivers it can be found on the ribbon-like floating leaves of unbranched bur-reed which develop in mid channel where the flow is strong. This niche appears to go unfilled on the Wey and Mole.

Donacia thalassina Germar, 1811

Nationally Scarce B

Rare on sedges at margins of open water. Adults also on reedmace.

RECORDS – **Bolder Mere**, 5.1995 (ISM), 5.2006 (JSD).

Donacia versicolorea

(Brahm, 1791)   PLATE 28

Very local on leaves of broad-leaved pondweed [and bog pondweed]. The adults can be elusive but the nibble holes in the floating leaves are distinctive.

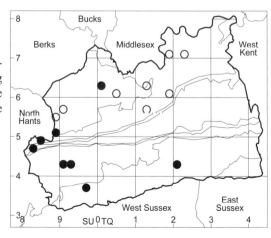

Donacia vulgaris

Zschach, 1788   PLATE 29

Local on bur-reed and reedmace.
Adults occur from May to August
with most records from June.

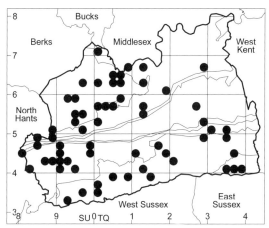

Plateumaris affinis

(Kunze, 1818)   PLATE 29

Nationally Scarce B

Very local on sedges (*Carex*)
growing beside ponds, lakes and
rivers.

RECORDS – **Battersea, Horsell**
& **Weybridge** in Fowler (1890);
Croydon, 1893 (H.Hutchinson);
Chilworth, 5.1934 (FJC);
Thursley Hammer Pond,
6.1996; **Peper Harow Park**,
6.2000; **Bay Pond** SWT reserve,
6.2000; **Waverley Abbey**,
31.5.2001; **Mill Lane**,
Godalming, 25.5.2007 (JSD).

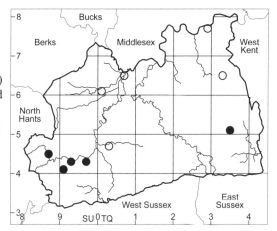

Plateumaris braccata (Scopoli, 1772)

Nationally Scarce A

Probably extinct in Surrey. Last recorded in early 19th Century at **Battersea** (JFS). It
occurs with *Donacia clavipes* at the legendary Burton Mill Pond in West Sussex, but I
have yet to rediscover this rarer species in Surrey.

Plateumaris discolor

(Panzer, 1795)

Local on sedges in acidic wetland areas, including bogs, mires and heath pools.

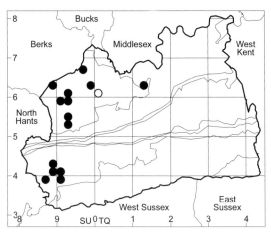

Plateumaris sericea

(Linnaeus, 1758)   PLATE 29

Local in richer wetlands than *P. discolor*, it lives beside ponds, lakes and rivers amongst emergent vegetation. Adults occur on a variety of waterside plants but are probably associated with bur-reeds.

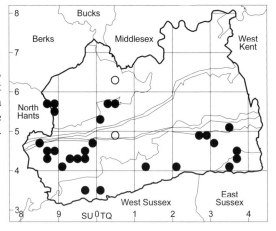

Galerucinae

A subfamily of 20 species in Britain, which includes some honorary water beetles. *Galerucella nymphaeae* and *sagittariae* feed on water plants, laying eggs in clusters on the floating leaves of water-lilies and amphibious bistort respectively. The adults and the black grubs crawl around on the raft-like leaves in which they chew holes. By midsummer many leaves are looking very threadbare! (see Plate 29)

Galerucella calmariensis

(Linnaeus, 1767)   PLATE 29

Widespread on purple loosestrife, usually on plants growing in water.

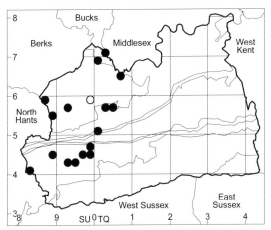

Galerucella nymphaeae

(Linnaeus, 1758)   PLATE 29

On water-lilies, especially white water-lily.

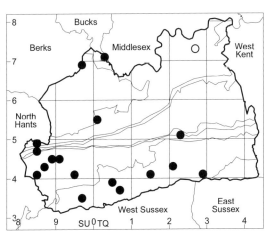

161

Galerucella sagittariae

(Gyllenhal, 1813)   PLATE 29

Widespread on floating leaves of amphibious bistort. Also on great water dock. The form on yellow loosestrife, once assigned full species status as *G. grisescens* (Joannis, 1865), is larger and may again be split.

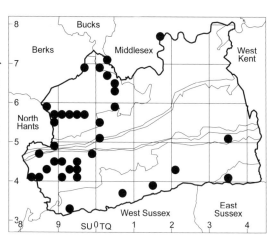

NANOPHYIDAE

Formerly placed with the Apionidae (seed weevils), the two British species are beautifully marked weevils. *Nanophyes marmoratus* (Goeze, 1777) occurs widely on purple loosestrife (*Lythrum salicaria*) at the margins of rivers and ponds, and in damp grassland, but the adults and larvae stay well above the water! Its diminutive cousin *Dieckmanniellus gracilis* does live sufficiently close to the water to deserve inclusion.

Dieckmanniellus (=Nanophyes) gracilis

(Redtenbacher, 1849)   PLATE 30

Nationally Scarce A

Rare on water purslane in open ephemeral pools, especially on heathlands.

RECORDS – **Horsell & Esher** in Fowler (1891); **Churt Flashes**, 5.1996 (JSD); **Ewhurst**, 1999 (RDH); **Bookham Common**, 19.8.2000 (RGB); **Brentmoor Heath**, 7.2002 (JSD).

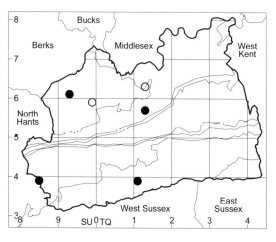

ERIRHINIDAE

(formerly part of Curculionidae)

Semi-aquatic weevils, which are widely considered as honorary water beetles, and regularly met with in the pond net!

Grypus equiseti (Fabricius, 1775)   PLATE 30

Horsetail Weevil

Nationally Scarce B

Local on horsetails growing in wet and dry situations. Although not a true aquatic, it is capable of plastron respiration!

RECORDS – **Battersea**, **Claygate** & **Esher** in Fowler (1888); **Bookham Common**, 1945 (AME).

Notaris acridulus

(Linnaeus, 1758)   PLATE 30

Local in wetlands on *Glyceria*.

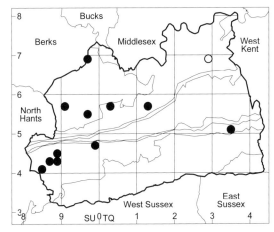

Notaris scirpi

(Fabricius, 1792)   PLATE 30

Local on lesser pond sedge and reedmace.

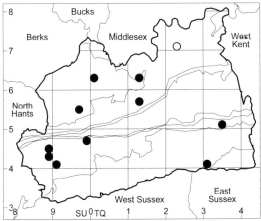

Tournotaris (*=Notaris*) *bimaculatus* (Fabricius, 1787)

Nationally Scarce B

Rare in Surrey, as it is more of a western species. Lives in wetlands on reed sweet-grass.

RECORDS – **Wimbledon** in Fowler (1891); **Chertsey Meads**, 25.5.2007 (RDH).

Thryogenes festucae (Herbst, 1795)

Rare on sedges.

RECORDS – **Bookham Common**, 1934 (FJC); **Fox Corner**, 9.9.95; **Hedgecourt Lake**, 14.10.2000; **Blindley Heath**, 14.7.2002 (RDH, det. RGB).

Thryogenes nereis

(Paykull, 1800)   PLATE 30

Local on spike-rush.

RECORDS – **Bolder Mere**, 6.1994 (JSD); **Bookham Common**, 21.5.1995 (RGB); **Brookwood**, 5.1996; **Esher Common**, 5.2000; **Thursley Common**, 5.2000; **Stockbridge Pond**, 6.2001; **Shalford Meadows**, 6.2001; **Royal Common**, 5.2002; **Thundry Meadows**, 30.4.2005 (JSD).

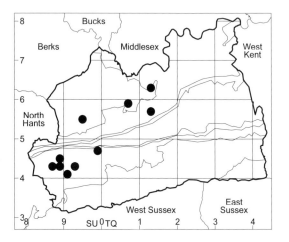

Thryogenes scirrhosus

(Gyllenhal, 1836)

Nationally Scarce B

Rare on bur-reeds (*Sparganium*) beside River Wey.

RECORDS – **Barnes, Esher, Horsell** & **Merton** in Fowler (1891); **Bookham Common**, 21.7.1947 (AAA); **Thundry Meadows**, 1996 (JSD).

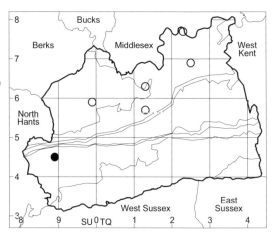

Stenopelmus rufinasus

Gyllenhal, 1836   PLATE 30

Azolla Weevil

Very local on water fern (*Azolla*). A strong flier which seems to find most large colonies of its host plant.

RECORDS – **Esher Common & Bookham Common**, adults swept from vegetation in rides at both sites (which were devoid of *Azolla*), 22.7.1995; **Mill Pond, Weybridge**, 6.2001; **Flexford**, 7.2002 (JSD).

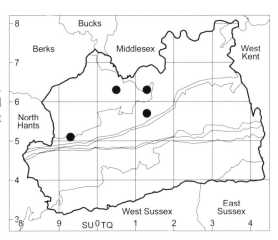

CURCULIONIDAE – Weevils

A huge family of mainly terrestrial species, including some semi-aquatic and a few truly aquatic species. The genus *Bagous* has long been the most enigmatic and frustrating for collectors, being very elusive and rare.

Note that occasionally 'terrestrial' species may occur on floating plants, such as *Ceutorhynchus assimilis* (Paykull) and *C. pallidactylus* (Marsham) on water-cress.

Gymnetron beccabungae (Linnaeus, 1761)   PLATE 31

Nationally Scarce A

Rare, possibly extinct in Surrey, although still extant in North Hampshire. It lives on marsh speedwell.

RECORD – **Bookham Common**, 12.6.1947 (AAA).

Gymnetron veronicae (Germar, 1821)   PLATE 31

Nationally Scarce B

Rare. A small black weevil, which feeds on brooklime and occasionally on figwort.

RECORDS – **Bookham Common**, 23.5.1930 (FJC); **Thundry Meadows**, on brooklime growing at edge of River Wey, 2.6.2005 (JSD); **Newark Priory**, 9.6.2005 (JSD).

Gymnetron villosulum Gyllenhal,1838   PLATE 31

Nationally Scarce B

Very local on blue water-speedwell, pink water-speedwell and their hybrid, beside streams, ditches and ponds. It lives on emergent plants in flowing water, but also in seasonal ponds.

RECORDS – **Esher** in Fowler (1891); **R.Wey, Wrecclesham**, 2000 (JSD).

Genus *Bagous*

Despite being dull, unattractive weevils, their very elusiveness make *Bagous* some of the most challenging of beetles. All are hard to find and some are mythically scarce. It is clear from these maps that they are under-recorded. It is perhaps no coincidence that a well-worked site like Bookham Common should have yielded such a rich fauna. My own net-based collecting across the county was unlikely to turn up *Bagous*, which need special search techniques. Sieving sedge litter, and suction-sampling pond margins, are far more likely to yield specimens than hand-netting. There remains considerable scope for improving our knowledge of these enigmatic weevils, but luck and patience are prerequisites for success. Alas, I appear to be lacking in both qualities!

Bagous binodulus (Herbst, 1795)

National Status: Extinct

Extinct countrywide. Taken at **Battersea Fields** in early 19th Century (JFS) and last recorded in UK in Norfolk in 1861.

Bagous brevis Gyllenhal, 1836

National status: Endangered (RDB1)

Probably extinct. Formerly found on heaths on lesser spearwort growing in shallow pools.
RECORD – **Horsell Common**, 1904 (GCC).

Bagous collignensis (Herbst, 1797)

National status: Rare (RDB3)

Rare on water-milfoil.

RECORDS – **Woking** (GCC); **Bookham Common**, 1.4.1941 (AME).

Bagous limosus (Gyllenhal, 1827)   PLATE 31
Nationally Scarce B
Rare, possibly extinct in Surrey. It is associated with broad-leaved pondweed.
RECORDS – **Woking** (JAP); **Bookham Common**, 1941 (FJC, AME), 26.4.1946 (AME).

Bagous longitarsis Thomson, 1868
National Status: Endangered (RDB1)
Extinct [associated with water-milfoil].
RECORD – **Woking**, circa 1900 (GCC), originally determined as *B. arduus* Sharp, but re-determined as *B. longitarsis* by AAA.

Bagous glabrirostris (Herbst, 1795)
Nationally Scarce B
Extinct [on hornworts, *Ceratophyllum* spp.]. Taken at **Weybridge** in 1896 (GCC); **Bookham Common**, 9.6.1934 (FJC, conf. RGB), 11.4.1942 (H.Last), 4.5.1952 (FDB, SLENHS).

Bagous lutosus (Gyllenhal, 1813)
National Status: Endangered (RDB1)
Extinct. Taken at **Ripley** by J.F.Stephens in early 19th Century.
The putative host for this species is thought to be branched bur-reed, but other hosts seem likely, as the recent rediscovery of the species in Norfolk was in the absence of this plant (Martin Collier, *pers. comm.*).

Bagous lutulosus (Gyllenhal, 1827)
Nationally Scarce A
Rare on rushes (usually toad rush) growing in seasonal pools on damp tracks.
RECORDS – **Ashtead, Barnes & Shirley** in Fowler (1891); **Horsell** (JAP); **Esher** (GCC); **Bookham Common**, 5.1929 (FJC), 30.9.2000, 14.8.2002 (MVLB), 11.8.2001 (RGB).

Bagous lutulentus (Gyllenhal, 1813) (= *B. nigritarsis* Thomson)   PLATE 31
Nationally Scarce B
Rare on water horsetail beside lakes, ponds and ditches. Adults can be swept from the emergent stems of the host plant.
RECORDS – **Bookham Common**, formerly abundant, taken by many collectors, appears to have been by far the most common *Bagous* on the Common during the mid 20th Century (Barclay, in press), but last seen on 12.6.1947 (AAA); **Bolder Mere**, 1992 (RGB).

Bagous nodulosus Gyllenhal, 1836

National Status: Indeterminate (RDBIn)

Probably extinct. Listed in VCH. [On flowering rush.]

Bagous puncticollis Boheman, 1845

National Status: Indeterminate (RDBIn)

Extinct. [Occurs in wetlands on water plants, including Canadian pondweed.] Taken at **Merton** in 19th Century by D.Sharp.

Bagous tempestivus (Herbst, 1795)   PLATE 31

Nationally Scarce B

Rare on creeping buttercup. Two males from **Bookham Common**, 1929 (F.J.Coulson, det. JSD, conf. RGB).

Bagous alismatis (Marsham, 1802) (= *Hydronomus alismatis*)   PLATE 31
Water Plantain Weevil

Nationally Scarce B

Rare on water plantain.

RECORDS – **Barnes, Battersea, Norwood** & **Wimbledon** in Fowler (1891); **Woking** (GCC); **Bookham Common**, 7.1915 (SRA, det. RGB).

Limnobaris dolorosa

(Goeze, 1777)

(= *pilistriata* (Stephens, 1831))

PLATE 32

Local on sedges in wetlands.

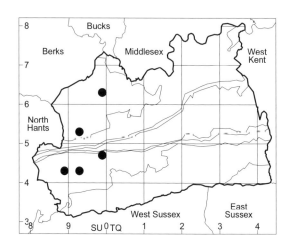

Limnobaris t-album (Linnaeus, 1758) PLATE 32

Rare on sedges in wetlands.

RECORD – **Frensham Little Pond**, 1983 (KNAA).

Amalorrhynchus melanarius

(Stephens, 1831)

Local on water-cress growing in ponds, streams and river margins.

RECORDS – **Horsell** & **Weybridge** in Fowler (1891); **Thundry Meadows** SWT reserve, 5.1994; **Bookham Common**, 1991 (JSD), 1995 (RGB); **Hawley Meadows**, 5.2000; **Eashing Bridge**, 5.2000 (JSD).

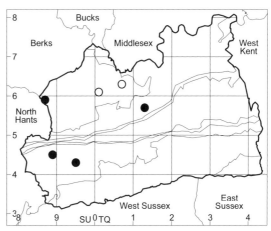

Datonychus melanostictus

(Marsham, 1802)

Local on water mint and gypsywort in wetlands, and at pond and river margins.

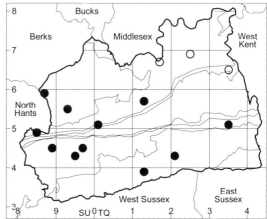

Drupenatus nasturtii (Germar, 1824) PLATE 31

Nationally Scarce B

Rare on water-cress, with only one modern record.

RECORDS – **Bookham Common**, 27.5.1930 (FJC), 17.6.1945 (AME), 10.4.1960 (SLENHS); **R.Wey, Wrecclesham**, 5.2007 (JSD).

Poophagus sisymbrii

(Fabricius, 1777)   PLATE 31

This distinctively patterned weevil is rare on water-cress.

RECORDS – **Box Hill**, 1924 (JLH); **Bookham Common**, 21.5.1995 (RGB); **Lakeside Park, Ash**, 5.1999; **Wrecclesham**, 5.1999; **Hawley Meadows**, 5.2000 (JSD).

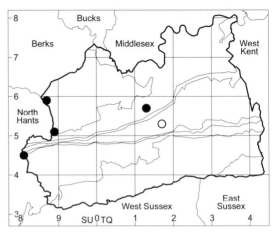

Tapeinotus sellatus

(Fabricius, 1794)   PLATE 32

Yellow Loosestrife Weevil

Nationally Scarce A

Very local on yellow loosestrife, especially where growing next to water. Locally abundant along parts of the Basingstoke Canal,

RECORDS – **Pirbright**, 1934 (Allen, 1935); **Virginia Water**, 1998, **Coleford Lake**, 5.1999; **Thundry Meadows** SWT reserve, 6.2000; **West Byfleet**, 6.2001; **Mytchett Lake**, 6.2001; **Deepcut**, 3.6.2001 (JSD).

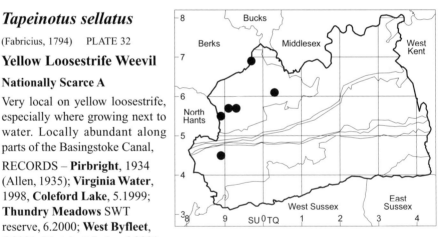

Eubrychius velutus (Beck, 1817)   PLATE 31

Nationally Scarce B

Probably extinct. This is the most aquatic of British weevils, a streamlined, free-swimming plastron-breathing species. Last recorded in Surrey at **Woking** in the late 19th Century by G.C.Champion.

Pelonomus (=Phytobius) canaliculatus

Fahraeus, 1843

Nationally Scarce B

Very local on water-milfoil. At some sites it occurs on parrot's feather, a highly invasive alien plant which is increasingly frequent, especially in village ponds.

RECORDS – **Caterham, Esher & Walton** in Fowler (1891); **Godstone**, 1977 (PJH); **Bookham Common**, 1995-6 (RGB), 1995 (JSD); **West End Common, Esher**, 5.1999; **Weston Green**, on parrot's-feather, 5.1999; **Bolder Mere**, 6.1999; **Aldershot Park**, on parrot's-feather, 5.2003 (JSD).

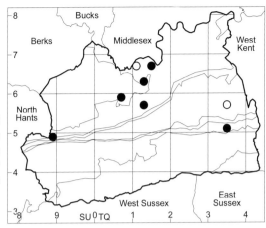

Pelonomus (=Phytobius) comari

(Herbst, 1795)   PLATE 32

Nationally Scarce B

Very local on marsh cinquefoil and purple loosestrife [also on tormentil].

RECORDS – **Barnes, Esher & Shirley** in Fowler (1891); **Thundry Meadows** SWT reserve, 14.5.1999, 30.4.2005 (JSD); **Wisley Common**, 2001 (AS).

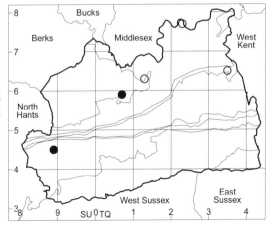

Pelonomus (=*Phytobius*) *olssoni*

(Israelson, 1972)

National Status: Rare (RDB3)

Rare on water purslane growing in ephemeral ponds on heathland. It can occur in large numbers, when its presence is betrayed by the threadbare state of the leaves of the host plant.

RECORDS – **Churt Flashes,** 5-7.1994-8; **Brentmoor Heath,** 5.2000, 7.2002 (JSD); **Headley Heath** 30.8.1997 (KNAA); **Nower Wood** SWT reserve, 6.2001; **Bagmoor & Royal Commons,** 6.2001; **Century Range,** 18.8.2003 (JSD).

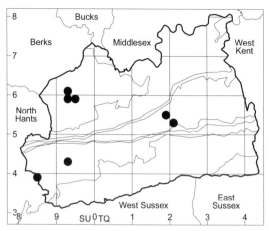

Pelonomus (=*Phytobius*) *quadricorniger* (Colonnelli, 1986)

Nationally Scarce A

Probably extinct. [On pale persicaria.] **Battersea Fields,** in early 19th Century (JFS).

Pelonomus (=*Phytobius*) *waltoni*

(Boheman, 1843)

Nationally Scarce B

On water-pepper growing along damp tracks. Not a true aquatic.

RECORDS – **Mickleham, Esher, Barnes** & **Walton** in Fowler (1891); **Woking,** 1897 (JJW); **Ockham Common,** 1982 (PJH); **Bookham Common,** 2.8.1989 (ISM); **Gracious Pond** SWT reserve, 7.2000 (JSD).

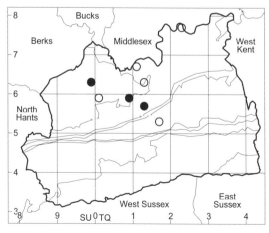

Phytobius (=*Litodactylus*) *leucogaster*

(Marsham, 1802)   PLATE 32

Nationally Scarce B

Rare on water-milfoil in ponds, a truly aquatic weevil crawling over and swimming between its host plants.

RECORDS – **Woking & Walton** in Fowler (1891); **Richmond Park**, 1913 (HSD); **Bookham Common**, 9.1995 (ISM); **Godstone**, 1977 (PJH); **West End Common, Esher**, 27.4.1999; **Bay Pond** SWT reserve, 5.2000 (JSD).

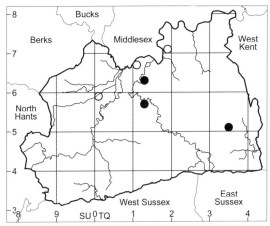

Rhinoncus albicinctus Gyllenhal, 1837   PLATE 32

National Status: Indeterminate (RDBIn)

Rare on amphibious bistort, primarily on the floating leaves but also on plants growing on land.

RECORD – **Virginia Water**, 5.2000 (JSD).

Rhinoncus perpendicularis

(Reich, 1797)

Local on leaves of amphibious bistort.

RECORDS – **Mitcham Common**, 1927 (JLH); **Wimbledon Common**, 1945 (KGB); **Bookham Common**, 1988 (ISM), 2000 (JSD); **Thundry Meadows**, 1999; **Bay Pond**, 6.2000; **Hawley Meadows**, 5.2000; **Virginia Water**, 5.2000 (JSD); **Chertsey Meads**, 7.2002 (RDH).

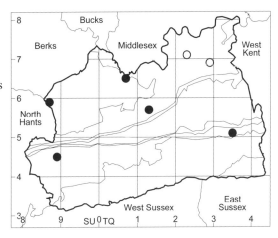

173

Hypera pollux

(Fabricius, 1801)

Local on aquatic umbellifers, especially hemlock water-dropwort.

RECORDS – **Dulwich** & **Shirley** in Fowler (1891); **Mitcham**, 1923 (JLH); **near Staffhurst Wood**, 6.1985 (RDH); **Bookham Common, Thundry Meadows**, 5.1992 (JSD); **Hedgecourt Lake**, 6.2000 (RDH); **Royal Common**, 2000; **Shalford Meadows**, 5.2000; **Stockbridge Pond**, 6.2001; **Papercourt Marshes**, 4.2005 (JSD).

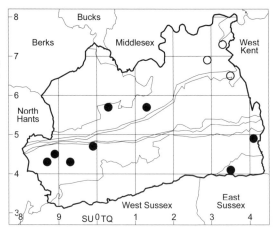

Lixus paraplecticus (Linnaeus, 1758) PLATE 31

National Status: Indeterminate (RDBIn)

Extinct in Surrey. Formerly found on banks of the Thames in 19th Century, but last recorded in Britain in Kent in the 1950s. Develops in aquatic umbellifers such as greater water-parsnip and hemlock water-dropwort.

Tanysphyrus lemnae

(Paykull, 1792)   PLATE 31

Duckweed Weevil

Widespread on duckweed (*Lemna* spp.) growing on ponds and at margins of rivers and lakes in quieter waters.

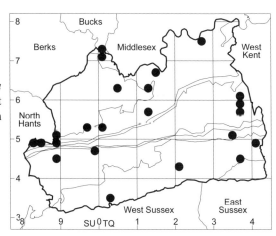

APPENDIX 1 – References

Allen, J.W., 1935.
Tapinotus sellatus in Surrey. *Entomologist's Mon. Mag.*
71: 67.

Angus, R.B., 1966.
Observations on swimming and swimming hairs in
Helophorus F. (Col., Hydrophilidae). *Entomologist's Mon.
Mag.* **102**: 58-64.

Balfour-Browne, W.A.F., 1940, 1950, 1958.
British Water Beetles. Vols. 1, 2, 3. Ray Society.

Balfour-Browne, W.A.F., 1962.
Water beetles and other things - half a century's work.
Dumfries.

Bateman, G.C., 1890.
Fresh Water Aquaria. Upcott Gill, London.

Bauer, C.K., & Gewecke, M., 1985.
Flight behaviour of the water beetle *Dytiscus marginalis* L.
(Coleoptera: Dytiscidae), pp. 205-214 *in* Gewecke, M., &
Wendler, G. (eds.), *Insect Locomotion*, Paul Parey, Hamburg.

Booth, R.G., 2000.
[*Helophorus longitarsis.* Exhibit at BENHS Annual
Exhibition 1999.] *British Journal of Entomology and Natural
History* **13**: 173.

Carr, R., 1999.
Nebrioporus canaliculatus (Lacordaire in Boisduval &
Lacordaire) new to Britain. *Latissimus* **11**: 36-7.

Carr, R., & Nilsson, A.N., 1988.
Larval morphology and phenology of the two cryptic species
Agabus chalconatus and *A. melanocornis* (Col: Dytiscidae),
with notes on other species. *Entomologist's Gazette*
39: 313-325.

Clegg. J., 1952.
Freshwater Life. Frederick Warne.

Crowson, R.A., 1981.
The biology of the Coleoptera. Academic Press, London.

Darwin, C., 1899.
The Descent of Man.

APPENDIX 1 – References (continued)

Denton, J., 2004.
The Beetles of Surrey - A Checklist. Surrey Wildlife Trust.

Duffy, E.A.J., 1945.
The coleopterous fauna of the Hants-Surrey border.
Entomologist's Mon. Mag. **81**: 169-179.

Forsyth, D.J., 1970.
The structure of the defence glands in the Dytiscidae,
Noteridae, Haliplidae and Gyrinidae (Coleoptera).
Trans. R. Ent. Soc. London **120**:159-182.

Foster, G.N., 1972.
The Aquatic Coleoptera of East Sussex. *Entomologist's
Gazette* **23**: 25-60.

Foster, G.N., 1981.
Atlas of the British water beetles. Preliminary edition, part 1.
Balfour-Browne Club Newsletter **22**: 1-18.

Foster, G.N., 1983.
Atlas of the British water beetles. Preliminary edition, part 2.
Balfour-Browne Club Newsletter **27**: 1-24.

Foster, G.N., 1984.
Atlas of the British water beetles. Preliminary edition, part 3.
Balfour-Browne Club Newsletter **31**: 1-22.

Foster, G.N., 1985.
Atlas of the British water beetles. Preliminary edition, part 4.
Balfour-Browne Club Newsletter **35**: 1-22.

Foster, G.N., 1987.
Atlas of the British water beetles. Preliminary edition, part 5.
Balfour-Browne Club Newsletter **40**: 1-24.

Foster, G.N., 1990.
Atlas of the British water beetles. Preliminary edition, part 6.
Balfour-Browne Club Newsletter **48**: 1-18.

Foster, G.N., 2000.
*A review of the scarce and threatened Coleoptera of Great
Britain.* Part 3. *Aquatic Coeloptera.* JNCC, Peterborough.

Foster, G.N., 2004.
An annotated checklist of British and Irish water beetles, and
associated taxa: Myxophaga and Adephaga - Hydradephaga.
The Coleopterist, **13** (4): 149-160.

APPENDIX 1 – References (continued)

Foster, G.N., 2005.
An annotated checklist of British and Irish water beetles, and associated taxa: Polyphaga, with an update to Adephaga. *The Coleopterist* **14** (1): 7-19.

Fowler, W.W., 1887-1891.
The Coleoptera of the British Islands. Vols. I-V. L.Reeve & Co., London.

Groves, E.W., 1982.
Hemiptera-Heteroptera of the London Area. Part XII. *The London Naturalist* **61**: 72-87.

Groves, E.W., 1983.
Hemiptera-Heteroptera of the London Area. Part XIII. *The London Naturalist* **62**: 69-86.

Groves, E.W., 1984.
Hemiptera-Heteroptera of the London Area. Part XIV. *The London Naturalist* **63**: 97-120.

Guthrie, M., 1989.
Animals of the surface film. Naturalists' Handbooks 12. Richmond Publishing, Slough.

Hyman, P.S., & Parsons, M.S., 1992.
A review of the scarce and threatened Coleoptera of Great Britain. Part 1. JNCC, Peterborough.

Jackson, D.J., 1956.
Observations on water-beetles during drought. *Entomologist's Mon. Mag.* **92**: 154-55.

Jackson, D.J., 1958a.
Egg laying and egg hatching in *Agabus bipustulatus* L. with notes on oviposition of other species of *Agabus* (Col: Dytiscidae). *Trans. R. Ent. Soc. London* **110**: 58-80.

Jackson, D.J., 1958b.
Notes on some nematodes and trematodes infesting water beetles. *Entomologist's Mon. Mag.* **94**: 109-111.

Jackson, D.J., 1964.
Observations on the life history of *Mestocharis bimacularis* (Dalman), Hym., Eulophidae, a parasitoid of the eggs of Dytiscidae. *Opusc. Ent.* **29**: 81-97.

APPENDIX 1 – References (continued)

Jackson, D.J., 1973.
The influence of flight capacity on the distribution of aquatic coleoptera in Fife and Kinross-shire. *Entomologist's Gazette* **24**: 247- 293.

Johnson, C.G., 1969.
Migration and dispersal of insects by flight. Methuen, London.

Joy, N.H., 1932.
A Practical Handbook of British Beetles. Witherby, London.

Korschelt, L., 1948.
Der Gelbrand, *Dytiscus marginalis.* W.Engelmann, Leipzig.

Levey, B., 2005.
Some British records of *Chaetarthria simillima* Vorst & Cuppen, 2003 and *C. seminulum* (Herbst) (Hydrophilidae), with notes on their differentiation. *The Coleopterist* **14** (3): 97-99.

Nilsson, A.N., & Svensson, B.W., 1992.
Taking off in cold blood – *Dytiscus marginalis* flying at 6.4°C. *Balfour-Browne Club Newsletter* **50**: 1-2.

Parker, E., 1908.
Highways and Byways in Surrey. Macmillan, London.

Pearce, E.J., 1937.
Additional records of British Insects: the water beetle *Hydrovatus clypealis* Sharp and the water bug *Aphelauchris* [sic] *montandoni* Horvath. *Journal of the Society for British Entomology* **1**: 228.

Robinson, M., 1991.
The Neolithic and late Bronze Age insect assemblages. *In* Needham, S. (ed.), *Excavation and Salvage at Runnymede Bridge, 1978: the Late Bronze Age Waterfront Site*, pp.277-326. British Museum Press, London.

Young, M., 1995.
Hydrophilus piceus at sea. *Latissimus* **5**: 20.

APPENDIX 2 – Gazetteer of Sites

Albury Pond	TQ0547	Capel Clay Pit	TQ1738
Aldershot Park	SU8849	Caterham	TQ3456
Arbrook Common	TQ1462	Century Range, Bisley	SU9358
Ash Ranges	SU9253	Chadhurst Moor	TQ1546
Ashtead	TQ1858	Charterhouse	SU9544
Bagmoor Common	SU9242	Chertsey	TQ0466
Banstead	TQ2560	Chertsey Meads	TQ0665
Barnes Common	TQ2275	Chiddingfold	SU9635
Barnes Wetland Centre	TQ2277	Chilworth	TQ0247
Basingstoke Canal		Chipstead	TQ2757
	SU8851-TQ0562	Chobham Common	SU9664
Battersea Fields	TQ2876	Churt Flashes	SU8639
Bay Pond, Godstone	TQ3551	Clandon Park	TQ0352
Beddington Sewage Farm	TQ2966	Clapham	TQ2975
Birches Wood	TQ1537/1538	Claygate	TQ1563
Bisley (Ranges)	SU9358	Cobblers Brook	TQ0537
Blackbrook	TQ1847	Cobham	TQ1059
Blackwater (River)	SU8449-8559	Coleford Lake	SU8856
Black Pond, Esher	TQ1262	Colony Bog	SU9259
Blindley Heath	TQ3645	Cosford Mill, Thursley	SU9139
Bolder Mere	TQ0758	Cranleigh	TQ0539
Bookham Common	TQ1256	Crossways, Hindhead	SU8734
Boundless Copse	SU8936/9036	Croydon	TQ3265
Box Hill	TQ1751	Cucknells Wood	TQ0442
Brentmoor Heath	SU9361	Cudworth	TQ2241
Broadmead, River Wey	TQ0256	Cutt Mill	SU9145
Broadmoor, Abinger	TQ1345	Deepcut	SU9056
Broadwater	SU9845	Devil's Punchbowl	SU8936
Brooklands	TQ0662	Dockenfield	SU8340
Brookwood	SU9457	Dorking	TQ1649
Broomhall Heath	SU9666	Dulwich	TQ3372
Bummoor Copse	SU9647	Dunsfold	TQ0036
Burgh Heath	TQ2357/2457	Dye House, Thursley	SU8939
Byfleet	TQ0661	Earlswood	TQ2648/2748
Camberley	SU8760	Eashing Bridge	SU9443
Camberwell	TQ3276	Eashing Valley	SU9444
Capel	TQ1740	Eden Brook	TQ3742

APPENDIX 2 – Gazetteer of Sites (continued)

Edolphs Copse	TQ2342	Hedgecourt Lake	TQ3540
Elmore Pond, Chipstead	TQ2756	Henley Park Ranges	SU9353
Elstead Common	SU9041	Hoe Stream, Woking	TQ0157
Epsom Common	TQ1860	Holloway College	SU9970
Esher Common	TQ1362	Holmwood Common	TQ1746
Ewhurst	TQ0940	Holmwood Corner	TQ1744
Ewhurst Green	TQ0939	Home Wood, Haslemere	SU9231
Farnham: Bourne Mill	SU8547	Horsell Common	TQ0060
Farnham Park	SU8348	Imbhams Farm	SU9233
Felcourt Wood	TQ3742	Jacobs Well	SU9953
Fetcham	TQ1455	Kew/Kew Gardens	TQ1876
Flexford	SU9350	Lakeside Park, Ash	SU8851
Folly Bog	SU9261	Lakeside Park, Guildford	TQ0051
Forest Green	TQ1241	Langham Pond	TQ0072
Fox Corner	SU9654	Leith Hill	TQ1343
Frensham Great Pond	SU8440	Lyne House Woods	TQ1938
Frensham Little Pond	SU8541	Merton	TQ2569
Friday Street	TQ1245	Mickleham	TQ1653
Frillinghurst Wood	SU9234	Mill Lane, Godalming	SU9643
Gatton Park	TQ2752	Mill Pond, Weybridge	TQ0563
Gibbs Brook	TQ3749	Mitcham Common	TQ2868
Godalming	SU9744	Moat Wood, Felbridge	TQ3640
Godstone	TQ3451	Morden	TQ2568
Gracious Pond	SU9863	Mytchett Lake	SU8954
Greatbottom Flash	SU8953	Newark Priory	TQ0457
Great Foxmoor Wood	TQ1243	Newdigate Brick Pits	TQ2042
Guildford Research Park	SU9650	Norbury	TQ3169
Hambledon Clay Pits	SU9737	Nore Hill	TQ0139
Hambledon House	SU9737	Norwood	TQ3369
Hammer Bottom	SU8732	Nower Wood	TQ1954
Hankley Common	SU8840	Ockham Common	TQ0858
Hartsgrove Hanger	SU9536	Ockley Green	TQ1440
Haslemere	SU9033	Oxshott	TQ1361
Hatchlands Park	TQ0651/0652	Oyster Wood	TQ2055
Hawley Meadows	SU8658	Papercourt	TQ0356
Hazelbridge	SU9735	Park Copse	SU9237
Headley Heath	TQ2053	Partridge Farm	TQ4147

APPENDIX 2 – Gazetteer of Sites (continued)

Paynes Green	TQ1637	Teal Pond, Wisley	TQ0658
Peatmoor Pond, Henley Park		The Jordans, Newdigate	TQ2038
	SU9353	The Moors, Redhill	TQ2951
Peckham	TQ3476	Thorpe Green	TQ0168
Penge	TQ3570	Thorpe Park	TQ0368
Peper Harow Park	SU9343	Thundry Meadows	SU8944
Pignuts Copse	SU9835	Thursley Common	SU9041
Pirbright	SU9455	Thursley Hammer Pond	SU9140
Prince's Coverts	TQ1561	Thursley Moat Pond	SU8941/9041
Putney Heath	TQ2273	Thursley Village	SU9039
Pyrford Village	TQ0458	Tilford	SU8743
Ranmore	TQ1450	Vachery Pond	TQ0636
Redhill	TQ2850	Vann Lake, Ockley	TQ1539
Redlands Wood	TQ1645	Virginia Water	SU9768
Reigate	TQ2551	Wallis Wood	TQ1238
Reigate Heath	TQ2350	Walton	TQ0966
Richmond Park	TQ1972/2072	Walton Heath	TQ2253
Rickford Common	SU9654	Wandsworth Common	TQ2773
Ripley	TQ0556	Waverley Abbey	SU8645
River Eden	TQ3950-4245	West Byfleet	TQ0361
Rowhill LNR	SU8549	West End Common, Esher	
Royal Common	SU9242		TQ1263
Runnymede	TQ0072	Weston Green	TQ1566
Send Grove	TQ0154	Weybridge	TQ0764
Shalford Meadows	SU9947	Wey Meadows	TQ0664
Shirley Common	TQ3565	Whitebushes, Earlswood	TQ2848
Sidlow Bridge	TQ2647	Whitepatch Bottom	SU9252
Sidney Wood	TQ0234	Whitmoor Common	SU9853
Somerset Bridge	SU9243	Whitmoor Vale	SU8635
Staffhurst Wood	TQ4148	Wimbledon Common	TQ2271
Stafford Lake, Bisley	SU9458	Winkworth Arboretum	SU9941
Stockbridge Pond	SU8843	Wisley Common	TQ0658
Stonebridge	TQ1747	Wisley RHS Gardens	TQ0658
Strawberry Bottom	SU9159	Witley (Common)	SU9240
Surbiton Water Works	TQ1767	Woking	TQ0159
Surrey Docks	TQ3679	Wray Common, Reigate	TQ2651
Tandridge Hill	TQ3653	Wrecclesham	SU8245

INDEX – Plants, with scientific names

INDEX – Plants, with scientific names (continued)

INDEX – Bugs and Beetles (scientific names)

Figures in bold indicate plate numbers

INDEX – Bugs and Beetles (scientific names)
(continued)

Figures in bold indicate plate numbers

INDEX – Bugs and Beetles (scientific names)
(continued)

Figures in bold indicate plate numbers

INDEX – Bugs and Beetles (scientific names)
(continued)

Figures in bold indicate plate numbers

INDEX – Bugs and Beetles (scientific names)
(continued)

Figures in bold indicate plate numbers

INDEX – Bugs and Beetles (scientific names)
(continued)

Figures in bold indicate plate numbers

INDEX – Bugs and Beetles (English names)

Figures in bold indicate plate numbers

INDEX – Other creatures (scientific and English names)

THE SURREY WILDLIFE ATLAS SERIES
published by Surrey Wildlife Trust

*"An outstanding monument . . . I am delighted to have them
on my shelves."* – Sir David Attenborough

Butterflies of Surrey by Graham A. Collins [SOLD OUT]
*". . . a delightful book and the best county faunal work on butterflies that
I have read."* – ENTOMOLOGIST'S GAZETTE

Dragonflies of Surrey by Peter Follett
"Well produced, well written . . . at a sensible price." – ENTOMOLOGIST'S RECORD

Larger Moths of Surrey by Graham A. Collins
". . . a much-needed, thorough and extremely well-researched book." – ATROPOS

Hoverflies of Surrey by Roger K. A. Morris
"It should be, as the publishers hope, a model of its kind." – BRITISH WILDLIFE

Grasshoppers and Crickets of Surrey by David W. Baldock
". . . without doubt, the best County Orthoptera to be published to date."
– BIOLOGICAL RECORDS CENTRE ORTHOPTERA RECORDING SCHEME

Ladybirds of Surrey by Roger D. Hawkins
*". . . an excellent book, a mine of information, attractively produced, and
easy to read."* – ANTENNA

Amphibians and Reptiles of Surrey by Julia Wycherley and Richard Anstis
". . . deserves a place on the shelf of any naturalist." – THE LONDON NATURALIST

Shieldbugs of Surrey by Roger D. Hawkins
*"Entomologists thinking of starting on the study of true bugs would be well
advised to start here . . . this is natural history at its best."*
– ENTOMOLOGIST'S MONTHLY MAGAZINE

Ants of Surrey by JohnPontin
*" . . . relevant wherever you record in Britain . . . this is an excellent book that
I would recommend to beginner and expert alike."*
– BEES WASPS AND ANTS RECORDING SCHEME (BWARS)

Also published by Surrey Wildlife Trust
THE SURREY COUNTY CHECKLIST SERIES
1. The Beetles of Surrey – a Checklist by Jonty Denton

**Titles can be ordered through bookshops, or via
Surrey Wildlife Trust's website: www.surreywildlifetrust.org**